U0107966

英诗经典名家名译

狄兰·托马斯诗选

英汉对照

SELECTED

（英）狄兰·托马斯 著　海岸 译

POEMS OF

DYLAN THOMAS

外语教学与研究出版社
FOREIGN LANGUAGE TEACHING AND RESEARCH PRESS
北京 BEIJING

图书在版编目 (CIP) 数据

狄兰·托马斯诗选：英汉对照 / (英) 托马斯 (Thomas, D.) 著；海岸译. — 北京：外语教学与研究出版社，2013.12 (2023.4重印)
(英诗经典名家名译)
书名原文：Selected poems of Dylan Thomas
ISBN 978-7-5135-3826-8

Ⅰ. ①狄… Ⅱ. ①托… ②海… Ⅲ. ①英语－汉语－对照读物 ②诗集－英国－现代 Ⅳ. ①H319.4：I

中国版本图书馆 CIP 数据核字 (2013) 第 292400 号

出 版 人　王　芳
项目策划　吴　浩
责任编辑　赵雅茹
装帧设计　赵　欣　水长流文化
出版发行　外语教学与研究出版社
社　　址　北京市西三环北路19号 (100089)
网　　址　https://www.fltrp.com
印　　刷　北京盛通印刷股份有限公司
开　　本　889×1194　1/32
印　　张　9.5
版　　次　2014 年 1 月第 1 版 2023 年 4 月第 10 次印刷
书　　号　ISBN 978-7-5135-3826-8
定　　价　22.00 元

如有图书采购需求，图书内容或印刷装订等问题，侵权、盗版书籍等线索，请拨打以下电话或关注官方服务号：
客服电话：400 898 7008
官方服务号：微信搜索并关注公众号"外研社官方服务号"
外研社购书网址：https://fltrp.tmall.com

物料号：238260101

记载人类文明
沟通世界文化
www.fltrp.com

意切情深信达雅
——序《英诗经典名家名译》

　　上小学前，爷爷就教导我要爱劳动，爱念诗。"劳动"是让我拾粪、浇菜、割驴草……"诗"是学念他一生中读过的唯一"诗集"《三字经》中的"人之初，性本善"等。我还算听话，常下地帮着干零活，偶尔也念诗。上中学后喜出望外地得知，最早的诗歌便是俺乡下人干重活时有意无意发出的"哎哟、哎哟"之类的号子声。老师说，这是鲁迅先生发现的。后来糊里糊涂考进北大，便懵懵懂懂向冯至、李赋宁、闻家驷等老师学习一些欧洲国家的诗歌。

　　大约十二天前，我正准备出访东欧和中亚时，北大、北外、党校三重校友兼教育部副部长郝平指示我为外语教学与研究出版社即将付印的《英诗经典名家名译》写篇序言。基于上述背景，我竟不自量力，欣欣然应允，飞机起飞不久就边拜读边写体会了。

　　一看目录，我在万米高空立即激动不已。译者全是令我肃然起敬又感到亲切的名字。

　　冰心是我初中时代的"作家奶奶"，我工作后曾专门找借口去拜访她在福建的故居。袁可嘉半个世纪前应邀从南大到北大讲英国文学史，我是自己搬着凳子硬挤进去旁听的幸运学生之一。王佐良先生是我读研究生时教授英国诗歌的。同学们爱听他的课，他大段引用原文从不看讲稿，我们常觉得他的汉语译文会比原文更精彩……穆旦、屠岸、江枫、杨德豫等我未曾有幸当面请教，从他们的作品中却受益良多，感激恨晚。

前辈翻译家们追求"信、达、雅"。落实这"三字经"却并非易事。

第一，在丰富多彩、良莠不齐的英文诗林中，译者要有足够高的先进理念和真知灼见去发现和选择思想水平高的作品。国产千里马尚需伯乐去认同，意识形态领域里的诗就更需要了。看诗的高下、文野、境界和情感永远是最重要的因素。我国《诗经》历久不衰，首先因为里面有"硕鼠，硕鼠，无食我黍!"这样政治上合民心的诗句，有"关关雎鸠，在河之洲……"这样传递真情的佳句。这套诗集选了许多跨世纪思想性极强的好诗。如雪莱《普罗米修斯的解放》中的警句："国王、教士与政客们摧毁了人类之花，当它还只是柔嫩的蓓蕾……"今天读起来仍发人深省。如莎士比亚在其第107号十四行诗中将和平与橄榄树的葱郁有机相连，上承两千多年前中国先哲"和为贵"的真谛，下接联合国大会此时此刻的紧急议题。这样的诗自然有人爱，有人信。

第二，诗源于生活。诗作者和译者都最好与百姓血肉相连。马克思曾与诗友调侃：诗人也得吃饭，别奢望写诗写饿了上帝会把盛着面包的篮子从天堂递下来。这套诗选中有许多生活气息浓醇、情意真切的诗。如出身佃农的彭斯在18世纪法国大革命后写的政治讽刺诗："我赞美主的威力无边! 主将千万人丢在黑暗的深渊……"，"……阔人们日子过得真舒泰，穷人们活得比鬼还要坏!"，"……有的书从头到尾都是谎言，有的大谎还没有见于笔端。"写实和预言都相当准确。

第三，译文要忠实于原作，自身又要通畅、简洁、优美。这套诗集中，英文原作都是名符其实的经典。读诗最好读原文，但世界上大约有三千种语言，一个人会用来读诗的语言肯定少得可怜。为开阔视野、加强交流、增进友谊，读外国诗大多还得靠翻译。这套诗选中的译者都治学严谨，都酷爱祖国和外国优秀文化，译文是他们辛勤劳动的杰出成果。他们把拜伦的奔放、纪伯伦的靓丽、济慈的端庄、布莱克的纯真、华兹华斯的素净、叶芝的淡定、狄金森和弗罗斯特的质朴译得惟妙惟肖。读这样的译作，哲学上可受启迪，美学上可得滋润。这有益于读者的身心健康，能满足青年学生的好奇心和求知欲，也能为有关专家的进一步研讨提供方便。

不妨说，这套诗集中外皆宜，老少咸宜，会书中两种语文或其中一种的人皆宜。

李肇星

2011年9月14日至25日自乌兰巴托（意为"红色勇士"）上空经莫斯科、明斯克（"交易地"）、塔什干（"石头城"）飞阿拉木图（"苹果城"）途中。

Table of Contents

译　序

狄兰·托马斯（Dylan Thomas，1914—1953）是 20 世纪英美诗坛最杰出的诗人之一，其非凡的诗艺掀开了英美诗歌史上新的篇章。他的诗围绕生、欲、死三大主题，诗风粗犷而热烈，音韵充满活力而不失严谨；其肆意设置的密集意象相互撞击、相互制约，表现自然的生长力和人性的律动。他前期的许多作品晦涩难懂，后期的作品更清晰明快，尽管某些细节仍然令人疑惑不解；然而，他作品的晦涩与不解并非由于结构的松散与模糊，而是因其内涵过于浓缩所致。他的诗篇感性而坚实，绝少流于概念或抽象；他的诗歌很少涉及精神压力、怀疑、自我分裂、反讽等现代诗常见的主题。他的诗朴实纯粹，自成一体，普通的一片落叶、一滴露水、一次性爱过程均可化为无穷的诗意；他从感性出发，通过具体可感的物象，触及内在的本质，最终达到某种永恒的境界。他那种化腐朽为神奇的诗歌艺术令人赞叹，令人翘首仰望。

狄兰·托马斯，1914 年 10 月 27 日生于英国南威尔士斯旺西（Swansea），1925 年 9 月入斯旺西文法中学学习，并开始诗歌创作。他那本著名的《笔记本诗抄》（1930—1934）[1]记录了他早期的大量习作。研究者发现，他后来正式发表的大量作品在《笔记本诗抄》中多能找到雏形，有些就是略作修改或部分删节修订而成。研究者在 1928—1929 年斯旺西文法中学校刊上还发现诗人更早的一些作

---

[1] Dylan Thomas, *The Notebook Poems 1930-1934*, ed. Ralph Maud. London: J. M. Dent, 1989.

品。据说诗人最早的一首诗写于 1925 年，即年仅 11 岁时。2003 年美国新方向出版社修订出版的《狄兰·托马斯诗歌》①收录了包括诗人的《笔记本诗抄》及早期作品在内的共计 192 首诗歌，更多诗歌残片现今保存在大英博物馆。1931 年 8 月，诗人从中学毕业，出任当地《南威尔士每日邮报》记者。1933 年，他在伦敦《新英格兰周刊》首次发表诗作，1934 年获"诗人之角"(the Poet's Corner) 图书奖，同年 12 月出版第一部诗集《诗十八首》，1936 年 9 月出版《诗二十五首》，1939 年 8 月出版《爱的地图》。1943 年 3 月，他出任英国广播公司播音员，1946 年 2 月出版诗集《死亡与入口》，1950 年 2 月 20 日—5 月 31 日，他开始首次赴美诗歌朗诵之旅。1952 年 1 月 20 日—5 月 16 日，他携夫人凯特琳开始第二次赴美诗歌朗诵之旅，1952 年 2 月出版诗集《梦中的乡村》，同年 11 月，诗人亲自从以往出版的诗集中选定意欲留世的 90 首诗作推出《诗歌合集》(1934—1952)。1953 年 10 月 19 日，诗人开始第四次赴美诗歌朗诵之旅，11 月 5 日不幸发生，他因酒精中毒陷入昏迷。1953 年 11 月 9 日，诗人在美国纽约去世，享年 39 岁。

　　狄兰·托马斯的一生就是一个传奇，他热情好客，交际甚广，诗人曾在《进入她躺下的头颅》一诗中写道："一叶草融入草坪才能长存，/ 一粒石禁闭在云雀的山岗会迷失自己。"但是，他无所节制的生活却暗藏不幸的种子。要是他少一点交际，多一点孤独，少一点放纵，多一点节制，他也许活得更久些，写出更多更美的诗篇。当然，那他就不再是诗人狄兰·托马斯。他的童年是在威尔士度过的，但他学习英语，不说也不懂威尔士语；他不喜欢威尔士民族主义，也反对各种民族主义；他玩世不恭的生活方式也是他对威尔士中产阶级严格的清教徒生活方式的一种反叛。尽管威尔士在某种意义上只是一个家乡的概念，但他诗句的乐感、元音辅音相互缠结的效果、奔放华丽的词汇以及奇特智慧的修辞均无可置疑地体现出威

① Dylan Thomas, *The Poems of Dylan Thomas*, ed. Daniel Jones. New York: New Directions, 2003.

尔士游吟诗人的风格。他那色彩斑斓、联想独特、节奏分明的诗歌，配上诗人深沉浑厚、抑扬顿挫的音色，极富魅力，令他赴美的四次诗歌朗诵巡演获得空前的成功。

1951 年，狄兰·托马斯在为回应威尔士一大学生的访谈而写的一篇《诗艺笔记》里谈道，"我写诗最早的起因源于对词语的偏爱。我记得最早的一首诗是童谣，在能阅读这些童谣之前，我喜欢的只是童谣的词语。至于词语代表什么、象征什么或意味着什么都是次要的；重要的是我第一次听到词语的声音，从遥远的、不甚了解却生活在我的世界里的大人嘴唇上发出的声音。词语，对我而言，仿佛就像钟声的音符、乐器的声响、风声、雨声、海浪声、送奶车发出的嘎嘎声、鹅卵石上传来的马蹄声、枝条敲打窗棂声，或许就像天生的聋子奇迹般地找到了听觉。我不关心词语说些什么，也不关心词语对杰克与吉尔意味着什么。我关心词语命名或描述行动时在我的耳朵里构成的声音形态；我关心词语投射到我双眼时的音色。"①

诗人一生创造性地运用韵脚、节奏、构词造字法，像一位诗歌手艺人在诗行间的词语上煞费苦心，乐此不疲，尽管有时效果并不如意。他倾其所能利用各种手段——双关语、混成词、悖论、矛盾修辞法、引喻或譬喻的误用、俚语、辅音韵脚、断韵，以及词语的扭曲、回旋、捏造与创新——往往以超现实主义的方式翻新词语花样，力求他的诗歌创作朝着理想的王国前行。

20 世纪 30 年代，英国诗坛及知识界陶醉于艾略特和奥登的理性世界。狄兰·托马斯一反英国现代诗那种苛刻的理性色彩而着力表现普通人潜在的人性感受，他的诗富有强烈的节奏和密集的意象，甚至超常规的意象排列方式，冲击着惯于分析思维的英国诗歌传统。事实上，狄兰·托马斯超现实主义的诗风与 20 年代风靡欧洲的超现实主义运动一脉相承。他认为那些艺术家既不满足于现实主义笔下描述的真实世界，也不满意印象主义画笔下想象的真实世界。超

---

① Dylan Thomas, "Notes on the Art of Poetry", Preface, *The Poems of Dylan Thomas*. 2003, p. 15.

现实主义者想要跳入潜意识的大海中，不借助逻辑或理性来挖掘意识表面下的意象，而是将非逻辑或非理性化为笔下的色彩与文字。超现实主义者确信四分之三的意识为潜意识，艺术家的职责就在于从潜意识中收集创作的材料，而非仅局限于潜意识海洋露出的冰山一角。超现实主义诗人常用的一大手法就是并置那些不存在理性关联的词语或意象，希望从中获得一种潜意识、梦境或诗歌，这往往比意识中的现实或想象的理性世界更为真实。然而，狄兰·托马斯尽管从主体上接受了超现实主义的诗歌理念，但并不完全同意，他曾经说："我不在乎一首诗的意象从何处捞来：如果你喜欢，你可以从隐蔽的自我的大海最深处打捞它们；但是在抵达稿子之前，它们必须经过非凡才智的所有理性加工；另一方面，超现实主义者却把从混沌中浮现出来的词句原封不动地记录到稿子上；他们并未塑造这些词语或按一定的秩序加以整理，在他们看来，混沌即形式和秩序。这对我而言似乎太过自以为是，超现实主义者想象从潜意识自我中随便捞出什么，就以颜料或文字记录下来，本质上就存在一定的趣味或一定的价值。我否定这一点。诗人的一大技艺在于让人理解潜意识中浮现的东西并加以清晰的表达；才智非凡的诗人的一大重要作用就在于从潜意识纷繁的无形意象中选择那些最符合想象目标的东西，继而写出最好的诗篇。"[1]

综合分析狄兰·托马斯超现实主义的诗风的成因，一定绕不过弗洛伊德思想。当时这一思想席卷西方文学、艺术、文化各大领域，对作为诗人的狄兰·托马斯产生了决定性的影响，尤其有关潜意识、性欲与梦的思想成为他诗歌的背景或题材。正如研究者发现，"狄兰·托马斯许多诗就是描述梦境，或根据弗洛伊德的《梦的解析》来构思，通过浓缩、转移、象征等手法来创作"[2]，就像基督教的神学启示构成诗人创作的素材一样。例如，他的诗歌会不时出现"诺亚"、

---

① Dylan Thomas, 2003, p. 21.

② William York Tindall, "Introduction", *A Reader's Guide to Dylan Thomas*, New York: Syracuse University Press, 1996, p. 9.

"摩西"、"雅各"、"大卫"、"所罗门"、"约伯"等《圣经》人物，因为《新约》的故事打从小时候起就成为他生活的一部分。但是，诗人不是一位虔诚的基督教徒，基督教的神学启示只是诗人深入思考宇宙万物的开始；他既感知到无所不能的上帝和爱的力量所在，也看到了比之更可怕的死亡的力量。狄兰·托马斯对生命与死亡的思考构成他的诗歌最华美的乐章。诗人将生、欲、死看成一个循环的整体，生孕育着死，欲创造生命，死又重归新生。他为生而歌唱："当胎膜随着一把剪子打开，/系上绿围裙哺乳的时光降临，/垂悬的饥荒周围没有嘴舌在骚动，/整个世界风雨过后，一片虚无，/我的世界在一条乳白的溪流里受洗。/大地和天空融为一处缥缈的山岗，/太阳和月亮洒下一样的白色光芒。"(《当初恋从狂热趋于烦扰》)

他更为创造生命的爱或欲而歌唱："她们告诉我爱情常青，即便树叶落满坟地，/阳光擦洗失落于草丛的十字基督，/女儿们不再悲伤，她们仍然会/在狐狸生养的大街滋生起欲望，/或在碎败的树林里饥肠辘辘：/山岗上的女人将穿过求爱者的树林，/永远疯狂地热恋那些健壮不灭的死者，//黑暗中的女儿像福克斯的火药静静地燃烧。"(《在白色巨人的大腿间》)

他也讴歌死亡巨大的毁灭力，等待死亡带来新生："不幸地等待死亡/偕同凤凰一起等待/火葬的柴火即将点燃我罪孽的时光，/等待阴影里的女人/石刻的圣徒充满肉欲，夹杂着死者/风起云涌，向我的自我不断地奉献"(《不幸地等待死亡》)。

在他的诗中，人生的演变与自然的交替，相辅相成，诗人更迷恋的是宇宙万物的兴衰："穿过绿色茎管催动花朵的力/催动我绿色的年华；摧毁树根的力/摧毁我的一切。/我无言相告佝偻的玫瑰/一样的寒冬热病压弯了我的青春。"(《穿过绿色茎管催动花朵的力》)生与死、人与自然融为一体，自然的力控制着万物的生长与毁灭，也控制着人类的生老病死。而"佝偻的玫瑰"与"寒冬热病"透泄出青春期强烈的欲望，以及一种对欲望难以满足的自然人性的关怀。事实上，诗人早期的《诗十八首》(1934)就表达了他关于自然的尊严、青春期的沮丧及其人性尊严受挫的意识："夏日的男孩，我看见你们在毁灭。/男人在蛆虫遍布的荒野。/而男孩的袋囊鼓鼓，非同凡响。/我是男人，你的父亲也是。/我们是燧石和沥青的子孙。/哦，当他们穿过，看爱情柱在亲吻。"(《我看见夏日的男孩》)

在他的第二本诗集《诗二十五首》(1936)里，诗人开始尝试新的意象、新的主题和新的风格，在他那首杰作《而死亡也一统不了天下》里，死亡如同生命、欲望一样令人兴奋，一样感人肺腑："而死亡也一统不了天下。/赤裸的死者一定会/与风中的人西天的月融为一体；/他们的骨头被剔净，白骨又消逝，/肘旁和脚下一定会有星星；/尽管发了疯，他们一定会清醒，/尽管沉落沧海，他们一定会再次升起；/尽管恋人会失去，爱却长存；/而死亡也一统不了天下。"

他的第三本诗集《爱的地图》(1939)影响较小，令人印象较深的是那首《葬礼之后》。而第四本诗集《死亡与入口》(1946)、第五本诗集《梦中的乡村》(1952)诗风渐趋明快，例如，《十月献诗》、《羊齿山》、《在约翰爵爷的山岗上》、《梦中的乡村》等诗篇节奏强烈，风景画般的叙述清晰易懂。他歌颂孩童的纯真，歌颂田园的宁静。而诗集中的一些短诗《祈祷者的对话》、《致你及他人》、《不要温顺地走进那个良宵》、《我的手艺或沉寂的诗艺》、《结婚周年纪念日》、《静静地躺下，安然入睡》、《挽歌》等在诗艺上更加炉火纯青，无懈可击。例如，那首著名的《不要温顺地走进那个良宵》：

> 不要温顺地走进那个良宵，
> 老年在日暮之时应当燃烧与咆哮；
> 怒斥，怒斥光明的消亡。
>
> 临终时明智的人虽然懂得黑暗逍遥，
> 因为他们的话语已迸不出丝毫电光，
> 却不要温顺地走进那个良宵。
>
> 善良的人翻腾最后一浪，高呼着辉煌，
> 他们脆弱的善行曾在绿色港湾里跳荡，

怒斥，怒斥光明的消亡。

狂暴的人曾抓住并诵唱飞翔的太阳，
虽然为时太晚，却明了途中的哀伤，
不要温顺地走进那个良宵。

　　记得上世纪 80 年代后期，傅浩兄从浙江衢州寄来狄兰·托马斯的诗集，就是诗人生前亲自选定的意欲留世的 90 首诗歌选本《诗歌合集》(1934—1952)①，我在完成学业之余译出第一稿，再由傅浩兄译出第二稿，后由鲁萌兄译出第三稿。但译稿后来又回到我的手里，一搁就是十余年，其间适逢我大病一场，我也就断断续续修订了十余年。其间我曾两度面临死亡，也正是从狄兰·托马斯生死主题的诗篇中吸取战胜疾病、战胜死亡的无穷力量。2002 年，河北教育出版社推出《20 世纪世界诗歌译丛》，第一辑收入《狄兰·托马斯诗选》，除个别诗篇选译外，基本上保留原貌。一个译本是有其生命周期的，据说一个好的译本最多也只能生存 50 年。2013 年，狄兰·托马斯的诗歌愈加受到读者的喜欢，尤其是年轻读者的喜欢，同时也出现了新的选译本，北京外语教学与研究出版社决定以英汉对照形式出版《狄兰·托马斯诗选》，并纳入《英诗经典名家名译》系列，出版前嘱我修订、补译、替换部分诗作。我据 2003 年美国新方向出版社出版的修订版《狄兰·托马斯诗歌》，同时参考诗人生前出版的五部诗集精选而成这部诗选，但是因篇幅所限，无法选入更多的诗作，只得留待以后出版《狄兰·托马斯诗歌全集》时弥补这一遗憾。

海　岸

2013 年 5 月 15 日

复旦大学枫林园

---

① Dylan Thomas, *Collected Poems 1934-1952*, London: J. M. Dent & Sons Ltd, 1977.

Forest Picture

Calm and strange is this evening hour in the forest,
Carven domes of green are the trees by the pathway,
Infinite shadowy isles lie silent before me,
Summer is heavy with age, and leans upon Autumn.

All the land is ripe. There is no motion
Down the long bays of blue that those cloudy headlands
Sleep above in the glow of a fading sunset;
All things rest in the will of purpose triumphant.

Outlines melting into a vague immensity
Fade, the green gloom grows darker, and deeper the dusk:
Hark! a voice and laughter—the living and loving
Down these fantastic avenues pass like shadows.

Dylan Thomas 狄兰·托马斯诗选

森林美景①

寂静又陌生，此刻林中的夜晚，
路边的大树，雕刻绿色的穹顶，
无比幽暗的岛屿静卧在眼前，
夏日一天天地沉重，斜倚着秋。

大地熟透了。不见一丝波澜
沿着长长的蓝色海湾，海岬阴沉沉
沉睡在消退中的落日余晖里，
一切长眠于此，意志得意洋洋。

茫茫然，融入一片无限之中
消散，青色的幽暗更深，薄暮更重了：
听吧！笑声与歌声——生活与爱情
仿佛影子一般，穿过美妙的林荫道。

---

① 刊于 1928 年斯旺西（Swansea）文法中学校刊，诗人时年 14 岁。据说
诗人最早的一首诗写于 1925 年，即年仅 11 岁时。

Clown in the Moon

My tears are like the quiet drift
Of petals from some magic rose;
And all my grief flows from the rift
Of unremembered skies and snows.

I think, that if I touched the earth,
    It would crumble;
It is so sad and beautiful,
So tremendously like a dream.

月中的小丑①

我的眼泪仿佛花瓣的飘零
静静地飘自神奇的玫瑰；
而我所有的忧伤飘自裂隙
飘自雪花和遗忘的天空。

我以为，如果我感动大地，
大地就会崩溃；
如此的悲伤而美丽，
如此的相似，宛如一个梦。

---

① 刊于 1929 年斯旺西文法中学校刊。

The Oak

Fierce colours fled about the branches,
Enveloping the ragged leaves unseen and strewn.

Hazardous reflections dipped in evening
Hover, making the forest fluctuantly vague.

Something austere hides, something uncertain
Beneath the deep bark calls and makes quiet music.

橡　树[①]

强烈的色泽逃离枝丫，
裹起凋零撒落的叶子，视而不见。

危险的倒影，浸泡在夜晚，
升腾，令森林茫然，起伏不安。

掩饰些微干涩，些微不定，
树皮深处声声呼唤，乐音无声。

---

① 刊于 1929 年斯旺西文法中学校刊。

I have come to catch your voice

I have come to catch your voice,
Your constructed notes going out of the throat
With dry, mechanical gestures,
To catch the shaft
Although it is so straight and unbending;
Then, when I open my mouth,
The light will come in an unwavering line.
Then to catch night
Wading through her dark cave on ferocious wings.
Oh, eagle-mouthed,
I have come to pluck you,
And take away your exotic plumage,
Although your anger is not a slight thing,
Take you into my own place
Where the frost can never fall,
Nor the petals of any flower drop.

我来领会你的声音^①

我来领会你的声音，
你构思的音符，在喉口翻涌，
干涩呆板的手势，
赶上这束光，
尽管如此的直接而决然；
然后，当我开口亮嗓，
光就会进来，成一条坚定的直线。
随后赶上夜晚，
展开凶猛的翅翼，涉水蹚过她黑暗的洞穴。
哦，鹰嘴，
我来拔下你，
拔走你外来的羽毛，
尽管你的愤怒不是件小事，
带你进入我的领地，
那里不见霜降，
更不见一片花瓣落下。

① 诗人笔记本上标明这首诗写于 1930 年 6 月 19 日。

狄兰·托马斯诗选

9

Dylan Thomas

Admit the sun

Admit the sun into your high nest
Where the eagle is a strong bird
And where the light comes cautiously
To find and then to strike;
Let the frost harden
And the shining rain
Drop onto your wings,
Bruising the tired feathers.

I build a fortress from a heap of flowers;
Wisdom is stored with the clove
And the head of the bright poppy.
I bury, I travel to find pride
In the age of Lady Frankincense
Lifting her smell over the city buildings.

Where is there greater love
For the muscular and the victorious
Than in the gull and the fierce eagle
Who do not break?

Take heed of strength!
It is a weapon that can turn back
From the well-made hand
Out of the air it strikes.

准许阳光[①]

准许阳光射入你高高的巢穴，
鹰是一只强壮的鸟，
光小心翼翼地射入巢穴，
寻觅随后撞击；
让寒霜硬化，
闪闪发亮的雨
落在你的翅翼之上，
挫伤疲惫不堪的羽毛。

我从一堆花中建起一座堡垒；
智慧储存丁香
以及那一簇闪亮的罂粟。
我埋葬，我旅行，自豪地
在乳香女士这样的年龄，
香气四溢，弥漫城市的建筑。

哪里有更大的爱，
肌肉发达，大获全胜，
甚过鸥鸟和凶猛的鹰，
谁又不能打破？

留意一种力量！
一种武器可以止步向前
从做工精良的手
从撞击的空气中。

① 据大英博物馆收藏这首诗的位置推算，写于 1930 年。

The air you breathe

The air you breathe encroaches
The throat is mine I know the neck
Wind is my enemy your hair shant stir
Under his strong impulsive kiss
The rainbow's foot is not more apt
To have the centaur lover
So steal her not O goat-legged wind
But leave but still adore
For if the gods would love
They'd see with eyes like mine
But should not touch like I
Your sweet inducive thighs
And raven hair.

你呼吸的空气①

你呼吸的空气侵入
我脖子上的喉咙
风是我的敌人，你的毛发不会
因他冲动有力的吻而骚动
彩虹之足不会更倾向于
那半人半兽的恋人
因而窃不走她，哦色迷迷的风
却会留下她，依然爱慕她
如果众神爱上了她
他们会用像我一样的眼神凝视
但不会像我一样去触摸
你那美妙而诱惑的大腿
以及乌黑的毛发。

狄兰·托马斯诗选

Dylan Thomas

13

---

① 据诗人笔记本推测，这首诗写于 1930 年 12 月。

It's not in misery but in oblivion

It's not in misery but in oblivion,
Not vertically in a mood of joy
Screaming the spring
Over the ancient winter,
He'll lie down, and our breath
Will chill the roundness of his cheeks,
And make his wide mouth home.
For we must whisper down the funnel
The love we had and glory in his blood
Coursing along the channels
Until the spout dried up
That flowed out of the soil
All seasons with the same meticulous power,
But the veins must fail.
He's not awake to the grave
Though we cry down the funnel,
Splitting a thought into such hideous moments
As drown, over and over, this fever.
He's dead, home, has no lover,
But our speaking does not thrive
In the bosom, or the empty channels.
Our evil, when we breathe it,
Of dissolution and the empty fall,

Dylan Thomas 狄兰·托马斯诗选

不在痛苦中而在遗忘中[①]

不在痛苦中而在遗忘中，
更绝非怀着喜悦的心情
大声呼喊着春天
越过那古老的冬天，
他躺下歇歇，我们的呼吸
必将冷却他那圆鼓鼓的脸颊，
并让他宽阔的嘴回了家。
我们必须低声走下狭窄的小道
我们拥有的爱和他血液中的荣耀
沿着管道流淌
直到从土壤里
涌出的喷口干涸
带着同样精准的力越过所有的季节，
而脉管一定会衰退。
他对墓穴尚未有所警觉
尽管我们轻视狭小的空间
点滴想法分割成如此可怕的瞬间
有如反复溺毙这场热病。
他死了，回家了，没有任何恋人，
而在内心，或空空的通道，
我们也没有更多的话要说。
我们消融的不幸，呼吸到它时，
我们的堕落，空空如也，

① 诗人笔记本上标明这首诗写于 1931 年 3 月。

Won't harm the tent around him,
Uneaten and not to be pierced
By us in sin or us in gaiety.
And who shall tell the amorist
Oblivion is so loverless.

不会伤害到他四周的帷幕，

不会被吞吃、被刺入

被我们的罪或欢乐所伤。

而谁会告诉这群好色之徒

遗忘何等无情。

Since, on a quiet night

Since, on a quiet night, I heard them talk
Who have no voices but the winds'
Of all the mystery there is in life
And all the mastery there is in death,
I have not lain an hour asleep
But troubled by their curious speech
Stealing so softly into the ears.
One says: There was a woman with no friend,
And, standing over the sea, she'd cry
Her loneliness across the empty waves
Time after time.
And every voice:
Oblivion is as loverless;
Oblivion is as loverless.
And then again: There was a child
Upon the earth who knew no joy,
For there was no light in his eyes,
And there was no light in his soul.
Oblivion is as blind.
Oblivion is as blind,
I hear them say out of the darkness
Who have no talk but that of death.

一个宁静的夜晚^①

一个宁静的夜晚，我自从听到他们
谈起生命里所有的奥秘
以及死亡里所有的神秘，
我一小时也无法入睡，
但为他们好奇的谈话所困扰，
谈话声轻轻地钻进耳朵，
没有一丝声响，除了风。
一个声音说，有个女人没有朋友
站在海上，哭泣
她的寂寞穿过空空的波浪
反反复复。
每一个声音都在诉说：
遗忘一如无情；
遗忘一如无情，
随后又说：地球上有个
孩子不懂得点滴快乐，
他的眼里不见一丝光亮，
他的灵魂不见一丝光亮。
遗忘一如瞎子。
遗忘一如瞎子，
我听到这些声音出自黑暗，
不谈别的一切，除了死亡。

狄兰·托马斯诗选

Dylan Thomas

19

Never to reach the oblivious dark

Never to reach the oblivious dark
And not to know
Any man's troubles nor your own—
Negatives impress negation,
Empty of light and find the darkness lit—
Never is nightmare,
Never flows out from the wound of sleep
Staining the broken brain
With knowledge that no use and nothing worth
Still's vain to argue after death;
No use to run your head against the wall
To find a sweet blankness in the blood and shell,
This pus runs deep.
There's poison in your red wine, drinker,
Which spreads down to the dregs
Leaving a corrupted vein of colour,
Sawdust beneath the skirts;
On every hand the evil's positive
For dead or live,
Froth or a moment's movement
All hold the sum, nothing to nothing,
Even the words are nothing
While the sun's turned to salt,

永不触及那忘却的黑暗[①]

永不触及那忘却的黑暗

也别去了解

任何他人或自己的烦恼——

否定铭记否定,

光的空白处,发现黑暗被点燃——

梦魇不再,

不再从睡梦的伤口流淌,

知识沾染破损的大脑,

一文不值,毫无点滴作用,

纵然徒劳争辩死后之事;

即便头撞南墙也无济于事

即便血液与躯壳找到甜美的空白,

这点脓藏得太深。

酒徒,你的红酒里有毒,

散开来,沉积到渣滓

留下一抹腐败的色泽,

裙沿下的锯末屑;

每一只手上必有邪恶

活着或死去,

泡沫或片刻的移动

所有掌握的一切,从无到无,

甚至连文字也是无

即便太阳转向盐,

① 诗人笔记本上标明这首诗写于 1931 年 10 月 26 日。

狄兰·托马斯诗选

Dylan Thomas

21

Can be but vanity, such an old cry,
Nothing never, nothing older
Though we're consumed by lovers and doubts.
I love and doubt, it's vain, it's vain,
Loving and doubting like one who is to die
Planning what's good, though it's but winter,
When spring is come,
The jonquil and the trumpet.

一声古老的哭喊，也只是虚无，
无未曾改变，无更为古老
纵然爱与困惑耗尽了你和我。
我爱又困惑，徒劳，徒劳，
爱与困惑，仿佛一位垂死之人
设想美好的一切，尽管只是冬天，
但当春天来临，
黄水仙和喇叭花盛开。

Children of darkness got no wings

Children of darkness got no wings,
This we know we got no wings,
Stay, dramatic figures, tethered down
By weight of cloth and fact,
Crystal or funeral, got no hope
For us that knows misventure
Only as wrong; but shan't the genius fail,
Gliding, rope-dancing, is his fancy,
Better nor us can't gainsay walking,
Who'll break our necks upon the pavement
Easier than he upon the ice.
For we are ordinary men,
Sleep, wake, and sleep, eat, love, and laugh,
With wide, dry mouths and eyes,
Poor, petty vermin,
Stink of cigarettes and armpits,
Cut our figures, and retreat at night
Into a double or a single bed,
The same thoughts in our head.
We are ordinary men,
Bred in the dark behind the skirting-board,
Crying with hungry voices in our nest.

黑暗里的孩子没有翅膀[①]

黑暗里的孩子没有翅膀，
我们知道自己没有翅膀，
逗留，在戏里的人，没有点希望
被戏服与真相，
水晶饰品或葬礼，压弯身子，
我们明白错误的冒险
只如同过失；难道天才就不能失败吗，
滑冰，踩钢丝，是他的爱好，
最好我们不要，不要行走在钢丝上，
我们在人行道上走，比他在冰上滑行
更易跌断脖子。
因为我们都是凡人，
干干的阔嘴唇、大眼睛
入睡，醒来，再入睡，吃喝，恋爱，嬉笑，
可怜的、小小的害虫，
散发着香烟和腋窝的臭味，
剪去身影，在夜里退隐到
一张双人或单人床上，
脑袋瓜里浮现同样的想法。
我们都是凡人，
在踢脚板后面的黑暗里繁衍，
巢穴里呼喊着我们饥渴的声音。

---

① 诗人笔记本上标明这首诗写于 1931 年 10 月。

Children of darkness got no wings,
This we know, we got no wings,
Stay, in a circle chalked upon the floor,
Waiting all vainly this we know.

黑暗里的孩子没有翅膀，
我们知道，我们没有翅膀，
逗留，在地板上粉笔画的圆圈里，
徒然等待我们明白这一切。

Youth Calls to Age

You too have seen the sun a bird of fire
Stepping on clouds across the golden sky,
Have known man's envy and his weak desire,
Have loved and lost.
You, who are old, have loved and lost as I
All that is beautiful but born to die,
Have traced your patterns in the hastening frost.
And you have walked upon the hills at night,
And bared your head beneath the living sky,
When it was noon have walked into the light,
Knowing such joy as I.
Though there are years between us, they are naught;
Youth calls to age across the tired years:
'What have you found,' he cries, 'what have you sought?'
'What you have found,' age answers through his tears,
'What you have sought.'

青春呼唤年轮①

你也曾看见太阳，一只火鸟
踩入云端，穿过金色的天空，
你了解人的嫉妒和他虚弱的欲望，
爱过又失去过。
你老了，像我一样爱过又失去过，
美丽的一切，却注定要死去，
在匆忙的霜雪间，你曾寻觅你的蓝图。
在夜晚，你步上山岗，
在生动的夜空下，露出头颅，
正午时分，你步入阳光，
像我一样知晓快乐。
虽然你我之间相差数年，也只是个零；
青春呼唤年轮，穿过疲惫的岁月：
"你发现了什么，"他喊道，"你到底寻求什么？"
"你发现的，"年轮透过泪水作答，
"正是你所寻求的。"

---

① 这首诗写于 1932 年 4 月，献给诗人的一位诗友 J. C. 伍兹（James Chapman Woods）。

Being but men

Being but men, we walked into the trees
Afraid, letting our syllables be soft
For fear of waking the rooks,
For fear of coming
Noiselessly into a world of wings and cries.

If we were children we might climb,
Catch the rooks sleeping, and break no twig,
And, after the soft ascent,
Thrust out our heads above the branches
To wonder at the unfailing stars.

Out of confusion, as the way is,
And the wonder that man knows,
Out of the chaos would come bliss.

That, then, is loveliness, we said,
Children in wonder watching the stars,
Is the aim and the end.

Being but men, we walked into the trees.

只不过是人[①]

只不过是人，我们走进了树林，
诚惶诚恐，柔声细语地
唯恐吵醒白嘴鸦
唯恐悄无声息
走进一个翅膀和啼鸣的世界。

如果还是孩子，我们也许会爬上树，
捉住睡梦中的白嘴鸦，不折断一根枝丫，
蹑手蹑脚地爬上树冠，
在枝叶之上，探出我们的脑袋
惊叹于漫天不灭的星斗。

不再困惑，仿佛那条路，
不再惊叹于众所周知的奇迹，
混沌之余必将迎来天赐的幸福。

然后就是，我们所说的可爱，
孩子们惊奇地瞭望漫天的星斗，
那就是目标与终点。

只不过是人，我们走进了树林。

① 诗人笔记本上标明这首诗写于 1932 年 5 月 7 日。

The midnight road

The midnight road, though young men tread unknowing,
Harbouring some thought of heaven, or haven hoping,
Yields peace and plenty at the end. Or is it peace,
This busy jarring on the nerves yet no outbreak?
And this is plenty, then, cloves and sweet oils, the bees' honey,
Enough kind food, enough kind speaking,
A film of people moving,
Their hands outstretched, to give and give?
And now behind the screen are vixen voices,
The midnight figures of a sulphurous brood
Stepping in nightmare on a nightmare's edges.
Above them poise the swollen clouds
That wait for breaking and that never break,
The living sky, the faces of the stars.

午夜之路①

午夜之路，尽管年轻人未曾察觉自已走过，
隐匿少许天堂的想法，或希望安息，
最终带来安宁和富裕。或是安宁，
忙着刺激神经却依然未曾爆发？
那就足够了，丁香和橄榄油，蜂蜜，
足够多的食物，道不尽的诉说，
人群移动的一场电影，
纷纷伸出手，给予还是给予？
而此刻银幕后是悍妇的声音，
一窝泛着硫黄味的午夜人物
在梦魇里踏上噩梦的边缘。
泛起的云层在他们上方镇定，
等待打破一切又永不打破，
活生生的天空，星星的脸。

狄兰·托马斯诗选

Dylan Thomas

33

Their faces shone under some radiance

Their faces shone under some radiance
Of mingled moonlight and lamplight
That turned the empty kisses into meaning,
The island of such penny love
Into a costly country, the graves
That neighbored them to wells of warmth,
(And skeletons had sap). One minute
Their faces shone; the midnight rain
Hung pointed in the wind,
Before the moon shifted and the sap ran out,
She, in her cheap frock, saying some cheap thing,
And he replying,
Not knowing radiance came and passed.
The suicides parade again, now ripe for dying.

他们的脸闪烁光芒[①]

他们的脸闪烁光芒，
月光与灯光交相辉映，
空空的吻变得蕴含深意，
廉价的爱情岛
变成奢华之地，
墓穴让他们毗邻温暖的水井，
（而骷髅留有树汁）。瞬息间
他们的面孔闪烁；子夜的雨
恰好悬在风中，
在月光转换，树汁枯竭前，
她，一身廉价的衣裳，聊着便宜之事，
而他回应着，
不知不觉，光芒来了又去。
自杀者再次列队前行，死亡随时光临。

---

① 据诗人笔记本推测，这首诗写于 1933 年 2 月末。

The almanac of time

The almanac of time hangs in the brain;
The seasons numbered, by the inward sun,
The winter years, move in the pit of man;
His graph is measured as the page of pain
Shifts to the redwombed pen.

The calendar of age hangs in the heart,
A lover's thought tears down the dated sheet,
The inch of time's protracted to a foot
By youth and age, the mortal state and thought
Ageing both day and night.

The word of time lies on the chaptered bone,
The seed of time is sheltered in the loin:
The grains of life must seethe beneath the sun,
The syllables be said and said again:
Time shall belong to man.

时光的年鉴[①]

时光的年鉴挂在脑海；
内心的阳光替季节编了号，
冬天的岁月移入人的深坑；
他的图表测量痛苦的页面，
移向子宫红肿的笔尖。

时光的日历挂在心里，
恋人的想法撤下过时的床单，
时光的英寸延长成英尺，
青春和岁月，凡人及其想法
白天黑夜地变老。

时光的言词落在章节的骨骼上，
时光的种子在耻骨区被遮蔽：
生活的颗粒必须在阳光下沸腾，
音节说了又说：
时光属于人类。

① 诗人笔记本上标明这首诗写于 1933 年 10 月 16 日。

Your pain shall be a music

Your pain shall be a music in your string
And fill the mouths of heaven with your tongue
Your pain shall be
O my unborn
A vein of mine
Made fast by me.

Your string shall stretch a gully twixt the thumbs
Whose flaming blood shall rub it at the rims
Your pain shall be
O my unsown
A ragged vein
Twixt you and me.

Your pain shall be a meaning in your lips
As milk shall be a music in the paps
Your pain shall be
O my unknown
A stream of mine
Not milked by me.

Your pain shall not unmilk you of the food
That drops to make a music in your blood

你的疼痛将是乐音①

你的疼痛将是弦上的乐音
你的舌将塞满上天的嘴
你的疼痛将是
哦，我未曾诞生
却紧紧相系的
一根血脉。

你的琴弦将展开指间的溪谷
火焰般的热血擦拭它的边岸
你的疼痛将是
哦，我未曾播撒
却连接你我的
一根粗糙的血脉。

你的疼痛将是你唇间的蕴意
仿佛乳汁将是乳头上的乐音
你的疼痛将是
哦，我未知
且尚未泌乳的
一条溪流。

你的疼痛必将会替你分泌食物
在你的血液里滴成了一段乐音

狄兰·托马斯诗选

39

Dylan Thomas

---

① 诗人笔记本上标明这首诗写于 1934 年 1 月 12 日。

Your pain shall be
O my undone
Flesh blood and bone
Surrounding me.

你的疼痛将是
哦，我解开的
缠绕我身的
血肉与骨骼。

I see the boys of summer

I

I see the boys of summer in their ruin
Lay the gold tithings barren,
Setting no store by harvest, freeze the soils;
There in their heat the winter floods
Of frozen loves they fetch their girls,
And drown the cargoed apples in their tides.

These boys of light are curdlers in their folly,
Sour the boiling honey;
The jacks of frost they finger in the hives;
There in the sun the frigid threads
Of doubt and dark they feed their nerves;
The signal moon is zero in their voids.

I see the summer children in their mothers
Split up the brawned womb's weathers,
Divide the night and day with fairy thumbs;
There in the deep with quartered shades
Of sun and moon they paint their dams
As sunlight paints the shelling of their heads.
I see that from these boys shall men of nothing
Stature by seedy shifting,

我看见夏日的男孩^①

1

我看见夏日的男孩在毁灭
金色的家园无比荒凉，
沃土冻结，没有一丝的丰盈；
他们携着妙龄少女，
热情融化冬日里冰封的爱情，
他们汹涌的波涛淹没满舱的苹果。

这些光的男孩，累积几多的荒唐，
搅酸沸滚的蜂蜜；
他们在蜂巢里拨弄严寒的霜凌；
阳光下几丝寒冷的疑虑和幽暗
养育他们的神经；
一轮信号月消失在虚幻里。

我看见夏日的孩子在母胎中
撕裂强壮子宫的风风雨雨，
神奇的拇指划分出白昼和黑夜；
在日月分割的浓荫深处，
他们涂抹自己的堤坝，
仿佛日光涂抹他们脱落的颅壳。
我看见男孩一个个成了无名之辈，
随种子的变换渐渐成熟，

① 诗人笔记本上标明这首诗写于 1934 年 4 月，1934 年 6 月首次发表于《新诗》。

Or lame the air with leaping from its heats;
There from their hearts the dogdayed pulse
Of love and light bursts in their throats.
O see the pulse of summer in the ice.

II

But seasons must be challenged or they totter
Into a chiming quarter
Where, punctual as death, we ring the stars;
There, in his night, the black-tongued bells
The sleepy man of winter pulls,
Nor blows back moon-and-midnight as she blows.

We are the dark deniers, let us summon
Death from a summer woman,
A muscling life from lovers in their cramp,
From the fair dead who flush the sea
The bright-eyed worm on Davy's lamp,
And from the planted womb the man of straw.

We summer boys in this four-winded spinning,
Green of the seaweeds' iron,
Hold up the noisy sea and drop her birds,
Pick the world's ball of wave and froth
To choke the deserts with her tides,

热情的跳跃或许让空气残缺；
三伏天涌动的阳光和爱情
从心里向喉口骤然迸发。
哦，看那冰雪中夏日的脉动。

2

但是，季节必须接受挑战或坠入
一处钟声齐鸣的地方；
在那儿，我们摇响星星，死亡般准时；
冬日里的男人，昏昏欲睡，
在夜晚，扯动黑舌的丧钟，
女人吹动风，却吹不回午夜的月光。

我们是黑色的反叛者，让我们
从夏日的女人召唤死亡，
从痉挛的情人处，召唤强悍的生命，
从漂浮大海的白净尸体上
召唤戴维神灯①上眼睛明亮的蠕虫，
从种植的子宫里召唤稻草人。

我们这群夏日男孩，在呼呼生风的旋转中，
海藻般的铁绿植物，
举起喧嚣的大海，放飞一群群海鸟，
捡拾世上球状的波浪和泡沫，
让潮汐窒息沙漠，

---

① "戴维神灯"指深海恶魔戴维·琼斯（Davy Jones）箱子上的神灯。据古
　老的水手传说，戴维·琼斯喜欢待在深海中，却常在暴风雨的夜晚出没
　在活人的船上。据说他有铜铃般大的双眼，说话时，鼻子会冒出阵阵烟
　雾。戴维·琼斯的箱子代表水手的安息地，即代表死亡。

And comb the county gardens for a wreath.

In spring we cross our foreheads with the holly,
Heigh ho the blood and berry,
And nail the merry squires to the trees;
Here love's damp muscle dries and dies,
Here break a kiss in no love's quarry.
O see the poles of promise in the boys.

III

I see you boys of summer in your ruin.
Man in his maggot's barren.
And boys are full and foreign in the pouch.
I am the man your father was.
We are the sons of flint and pitch.
O see the poles are kissing as they cross.

为扎一只花环，梳理乡间的花园。

在春天，我们用冬青枝缠绕前额，

嘿，还有鲜血和浆果，

快乐的乡绅被钉上树干；

湿漉漉的肉肌在此枯干而亡，

热吻在无情的采石场裂成碎片。

哦，看孩子们信誓旦旦的爱情柱。

3

夏日的男孩，我看见你们在毁灭。

男人在蛆虫遍布的荒野。

而男孩的袋囊鼓鼓，非同凡响。

我是男人，你的父亲也是。

我们是燧石和沥青的子孙。

哦，当他们穿过，看爱情柱在亲吻。

When once the twilight locks no longer

When once the twilight locks no longer
Locked in the long worm of my finger
Nor dammed the sea that sped about my fist,
The mouth of time sucked, like a sponge,
The milky acid on each hinge,
And swallowed dry the waters of the breast.

When the galactic sea was sucked
And all the dry seabed unlocked,
I sent my creature scouting on the globe,
That globe itself of hair and bone
That, sewn to me by nerve and brain,
Had stringed my flask of matter to his rib.

My fuses timed to charge his heart,
He blew like powder to the light
And held a little sabbath with the sun,
But when the stars, assuming shape,
Drew in his eyes the straws of sleep,
He drowned his father's magics in a dream.

All issue armoured, of the grave,
The redhaired cancer still alive,

一旦晨曦不再伫留^①

一旦晨曦不再伫留
伫留在我蠕虫般长长的手指，
不再筑坝拦截拳头上奔腾的大海，
时间的嘴，就会海绵般吮吸
每一条铰链上的乳酸，
吸干胸乳间奔流的乳汁。

当大海的乳汁被吸尽，
干涸的海底一览无余，
我派遣我的生灵巡视整个世界，
大地自身长满毛发和骨骼，
靠神经和大脑缝补我的肉身，
将我满瓶的物系上他的肋骨。

我的引信定时引爆他的心，
他像点燃的火药爆裂，
随太阳度过一段短暂的安息，
但是当星星竞相现形，
在他的眼里拉动睡眠的麦秆，
他就会随父亲的魔法沉溺在梦里。

所有的问题披上盔甲，坟墓里
红发的癌肿依然存活人世，

---

① 1934 年 6 月首次发表于《新诗》，更早的版本见于 1933 年 11 月 11 日。

The cataracted eyes that filmed their cloth;
Some dead undid their bushy jaws,
And bags of blood let out their flies;
He had by heart the Christ-cross-row of death.

Sleep navigates the tides of time;
The dry Sargasso of the tomb
Gives up its dead to such a working sea;
And sleep rolls mute above the beds
Where fishes' food is fed the shades
Who periscope through flowers to the sky.

The hanged who lever from the limes
Ghostly propellers for their limbs,
The cypress lads who wither with the cock,
These, and the others in sleep's acres,
Of dreaming men make moony suckers,
And snipe the fools of vision in the back.

When once the twilight screws were turned,
And mother milk was stiff as sand,
I sent my own ambassador to light;
By trick or chance he fell asleep
And conjured up a carcass shape
To rob me of my fluids in his heart.

Awake, my sleeper, to the sun,
A worker in the morning town,

患上白内障的眼睛被蒙上纱布；
死者松开灌木丛生的下颌，
成袋的血液放飞一群群苍蝇；
他的内心竖起耶稣受难的十字架。

睡眠航行在时间的浪潮；
坟地上干枯的马尾藻
将死者抛给咆哮无比的大海；
而睡眠无声地滑过海床，
鱼饵在此喂养片片阴影，
它们透过花丛的潜望镜眺望天空。

被绞杀的人撬离了界限，
幽灵般转动起四肢，
柏树少年随公鸡而枯萎，
这些那些入眠中的
追梦人成了月光的吮吸者，
在背后狙击想象的蠢材。

一旦晨曦的螺杆被转动，
母乳沙砾般僵硬，
我就派遣使节走访光明；
他却有意无意地坠落梦境，
念动咒语召唤尸体的身影，
从他的心中洗劫我的体液。

醒来吧，沉睡者，迎着阳光，
小镇早起忙碌的劳动者，

And leave the poppied pickthank where he lies;
The fences of the light are down,
All but the briskest riders thrown
And worlds hang on the trees.

离别在此醉生梦死的马屁精；
光的栅栏大片坍塌，
除了敏捷的骑手，人人都被摔下，
而世界悬挂在树梢。

A process in the weather of the heart

A process in the weather of the heart
Turns damp to dry; the golden shot
Storms in the freezing tomb.
A weather in the quarter of the veins
Turns night to day; blood in their suns
Lights up the living worm.

A process in the eye forwarns
The bones of blindness; and the womb
Drives in a death as life leaks out.

A darkness in the weather of the eye
Is half its light; the fathomed sea
Breaks on unangled land.
The seed that makes a forest of the loin
Forks half its fruit; and half drops down,
Slow in a sleeping wind.

A weather in the flesh and bone
Is damp and dry; the quick and dead
Move like two ghosts before the eye.
A process in the weather of the world

心的气候进程^①

心的气候进程
由潮变干；金色的炮弹
在冰封的墓穴里怒吼。
四分之一血脉里的气候
变黑夜为白昼；太阳下的血
点燃活生生的蠕虫。

眼中的进程
预警盲目的骨头；而子宫
随生命脱泄而驶入死亡。

眼中气候里的黑暗
一半是光；深深的海洋
拍打棱角光滑的堤岸。
种子在耻骨区，打造一片森林
又开一半的果实；另一半坠落，
顺沉睡的风缓缓而落。

肉体和骨骼里的气候
又潮又干；生者和死者
像两个幽灵在眼前游荡。
世界的气候进程

① 诗人笔记本上标明这首诗写于 1934 年 2 月 2 日，1934 年 2 月 11 日首
次发表于《周日参考》。

Turns ghost to ghost; each mothered child
Sits in their double shade.
A process blows the moon into the sun,
Pulls down the shabby curtains of the skin;
And the heart gives up its dead.

变幽灵为幽灵；每位受宠的孩子
坐在双重的阴影里。
月光吹入阳光的进程，
扯下了皮肤那褴褛的帘幕；
而心放弃死亡。

Before I knocked

Before I knocked and flesh let enter,
With liquid hands tapped on the womb,
I who was shapeless as the water
That shaped the Jordan near my home
Was brother to Mnetha's daughter
And sister to the fathering worm.

I who was deaf to spring and summer,
Who knew not sun nor moon by name,
Felt thud beneath my flesh's armour,
As yet was in a molten form,
The leaden stars, the rainy hammer
Swung by my father from his dome.

I knew the message of the winter,
The darted hail, the childish snow,
And the wind was my sister suitor;
Wind in me leaped, the hellborn dew;
My veins flowed with the Eastern weather;
Ungotten I knew night and day.

① 诗人笔记本上标明这首诗写于 1933 年 9 月 4 日,首次发表于《诗十八首》。
② 约旦河,源于叙利亚境内,向南流经以色列,在约旦境内注入死海,是世界上海拔最低的河。在《圣经》中,约旦河是数次发生神迹的地点。

在我敲开之前①

在我伸出流动的手指，
轻叩子宫，敲开肉体大门之前，
我像水一样飘忽无形，
那水汇成了家乡附近的约旦河②，
我是摩尼莎③女儿的兄弟，
我也是繁衍蠕虫的姐妹。

我充耳不闻春天和夏天，
叫不出太阳和月亮的名字，
我感到血肉盔甲之下，
砰然作响，迄今还在熔合，
父亲在穹顶下挥舞
雨点般的铁锤，铅星飞溅。

我知晓冬天的讯息，
冰雹纷飞，雪花如嬉，
而寒风追逐我的姐妹；
风在我体内跳动，恶露降临；
我的血管随东方的天气流动；
未出生我就知晓黑夜与白昼。

③ 摩尼莎（Mnetha），源自诗人布莱克诗篇《蒂丽儿》（Tiriel）中的人物，据研究人员分析，Mnetha 系希腊神话中记忆女神摩涅莫绪涅（Mnemosyne）与智慧女神雅典娜（Athena）的名字拼缀而成。

As yet ungotten, I did suffer;
The rack of dreams my lily bones
Did twist into a living cipher,
And flesh was snipped to cross the lines
Of gallow crosses on the liver
And brambles in the wringing brains.

My throat knew thirst before the structure
Of skin and vein around the well
Where words and water make a mixture
Unfailing till the blood runs foul;
My heart knew love, my belly hunger;
I smelt the maggot in my stool.

And time cast forth my mortal creature
To drift or drown upon the seas
Acquainted with the salt adventure
Of tides that never touch the shores.
I who was rich was made the richer
By sipping at the vine of days.

I, born of flesh and ghost, was neither
A ghost nor man, but mortal ghost.
And I was struck down by death's feather.
I was a mortal to the last
Long breath that carried to my father
The message of his dying christ.

还未出生，我就饱经风霜；
噩梦折磨着我，百合般的骨头
绞成一组活生生的密码。
而被肢解的血肉穿越一排排
耸立在肝区的十字架，
穿越脑海里缠结的荆棘丛。

在肌肤和血管围拢井口之前，
我的喉咙早已知道干渴，
言词和水在那儿融为一体，
无穷无尽，直到血发臭；
我的心感受到爱，胃饱尝饥饿；
我在自己的粪便嗅到蛆虫。

时光抛出我凡夫俗子的躯体
追随咸潮奔涌的冒险
在海上漂泊沉浮
却未曾触及到岸。
我啜饮时光的葡萄汁
愈加变得奢华富有。

我的灵与肉天生一体，非人
亦非魔，却是凡间的幽灵。
我被死亡的羽毛击倒在地。
终有一死，我最后
一口长长的呼吸捎给父亲
那基督临终的口信。

You who bow down at cross and altar,
Remember me and pity Him
Who took my flesh and bone for armour
And doublecrossed my mother's womb.

你俯首眼前的十字架和祭坛，
记着我，并怜悯基督，
是他误将我的骨肉当成盔甲，
欺骗了我母亲的子宫。

The force that through the green fuse drives the flower

The force that through the green fuse drives the flower
Drives my green age; that blasts the roots of trees
Is my destroyer.
And I am dumb to tell the crooked rose
My youth is bent by the same wintry fever.

The force that drives the water through the rocks
Drives my red blood; that dries the mouthing streams
Turns mine to wax.
And I am dumb to mouth unto my veins
How at the mountain spring the same mouth sucks.

The hand that whirls the water in the pool
Stirs the quicksand; that ropes the blowing wind
Hauls my shroud sail.
And I am dumb to tell the hanging man
How of my clay is made the hangman's lime.

The lips of time leech to the fountain head;
Love drips and gathers, but the fallen blood
Shall calm her sores.

穿过绿色茎管催动花朵的力①

穿过绿色茎管催动花朵的力
催动我绿色的年华；摧毁树根的力
摧毁我的一切。
我无言相告佝偻的玫瑰
一样的寒冬热病压弯了我的青春。

催动流水穿透岩石的力
催动我鲜红的血液；驱使溪流干涸的力
驱使我的血流衰微。
我无言相告我的血管
同是这张嘴怎样吸干山涧的清泉。

搅动一泓池水旋转的手
搅动沙的流动；牵动风前行的手
扯动我尸布般的风帆。
我无言相告那绞死的人
我的泥土怎样制成刽子手的石灰。

时间的嘴唇水蛭般贴紧泉眼；
爱滴落又聚集，但是流淌的血
一定会抚慰她的伤痛。

---

① 诗人笔记本上标明这首诗写于 1933 年 10 月 12 日，1933 年 10 月 29 日
首次发表于《周日参考》。

And I am dumb to tell a weather's wind
How time has ticked a heaven round the stars.

And I am dumb to tell the lover's tomb
How at my sheet goes the same crooked worm.

我无言相告一个季候的风
时光怎样围绕星星滴答出一个天堂。

我无言相告恋人的坟墓
我的被褥上蠕动着一样扭曲的蛆虫。

My hero bares his nerves

My hero bares his nerves along my wrist
That rules from wrist to shoulder,
Unpacks the head that, like a sleepy ghost,
Leans on my mortal ruler,
The proud spine spurning turn and twist.

And these poor nerves so wired to the skull
Ache on the lovelorn paper
I hug to love with my unruly scrawl
That utters all love hunger
And tells the page the empty ill.

My hero bares my side and sees his heart
Tread, like a naked Venus,
The beach of flesh, and wind her bloodred plait;
Stripping my loin of promise,
He promises a secret heat.

He holds the wire from this box of nerves
Praising the mortal error
Of birth and death, the two sad knaves of thieves,
And the hunger's emperor;
He pulls that chain, the cistern moves.

Dylan Thomas 狄兰·托马斯诗选

我的英雄裸露他的神经①

我的英雄裸露他的神经
沿着手腕到臂膀，
掀开斜靠我肉身之上的头颅，
像个昏昏欲睡的幽灵，
那高傲的脊梁巍然挺立。

而可怜的神经线圈般连接头颅
在失恋的纸笺上疼痛不已
我以狂放的草书拥抱爱情
倾诉所有爱的饥渴
在纸页书写空虚的病痛。

我的英雄剥开我的一侧，看见
他的心，像赤裸的维纳斯，
踏着血肉之滨，舞动血染的辫子；
他剥开我耻骨区的诺言，
允诺一次秘密的欢情。

他握住这盒神经的线圈，
颂扬凡间的生死错误，
这一对悲痛欲绝的无赖贼子，
以及饥渴的帝王；
他拉动链子，水随之流动。

① 诗人笔记本上标明这首诗写于 1933 年 9 月 17 日，首次发表于《诗十八首》。

Where once the waters of your face

Where once the waters of your face
Spun to my screws, your dry ghost blows,
The dead turns up its eye;
Where once the mermen through your ice
Pushed up their hair, the dry wind steers
Through salt and root and roe.

Where once your green knots sank their splice
Into the tided cord, there goes
The green unraveller,
His scissors oiled, his knife hung loose
To cut the channels at their source
And lay the wet fruits low.

Invisible, your clocking tides
Break on the lovebeds of the weeds;
The weed of love's left dry;
There round about your stones the shades
Of children go who, from their voids,
Cry to the dolphined sea.

Dry as a tomb, your coloured lids

在你脸上的水①

在你脸上的水曾经被我螺杆
搅动的地方，掠过你枯干的灵魂，
死者的眼睛上翻着；
在美人鱼撩起头发曾经穿越
你冰层的地方，刮过干枯的风
穿越盐粒、草根和鱼卵。

在你下沉的绿色绳结曾经紧缚
潮汐下的船索，走来
那绿色的解缚人，
剪刀抹上油，刀片松弛地悬着，
从源头切断他们的通道，
摘下湿漉漉的果实。

来去无踪，潮升汐落
拍打水草丛生的爱情之床；
爱的水草枯萎而亡；
孩子们的身影晃动在岩石的四周，
他们各自从空旷中，向着
海豚游戈的大海呼喊。

虽然坟墓般干枯，你斑斓的眼睑

① 诗人笔记本上标明这首诗写于 1934 年 3 月 18 日，1934 年 3 月 25 日首次发表于《周日参考》。

Shall not be latched while magic glides
Sage on the earth and sky;
There shall be corals in your beds,
There shall be serpents in your tides,
Till all our sea-faiths die.

绝不会锁闭，圣贤施展魔力
滑过大地和天空；
你的床笫将铺满珊瑚，
你的潮汐将游动起蛇群，
直到大海所有的信念消逝。

If I were tickled by the rub of love

If I were tickled by the rub of love,
A rooking girl who stole me for her side,
Broke through her straws, breaking my bandaged string,
If the red tickle as the cattle calve
Still set to scratch a laughter from my lung,
I would not fear the apple nor the flood
Nor the bad blood of spring.

Shall it be male or female? say the cells,
And drop the plum like fire from the flesh.
If I were tickled by the hatching hair,
The winging bone that sprouted in the heels,
The itch of man upon the baby's thigh,
I would not fear the gallows nor the axe
Nor the crossed sticks of war.

Shall it be male or female? say the fingers
That chalk the walls with green girls and their men.
I would not fear the muscling-in of love
If I were tickled by the urchin hungers
Rehearsing heat upon a raw-edged nerve.
I would not fear the devil in the loin
Nor the outspoken grave.

假如我被爱的抚摸撩得心醉①

假如我被爱的抚摸撩得心醉，
偷我到她身旁的骗子女郎，
就会穿过她的草窟，扯掉我绷带的约束，
假如红色的撩拨，像母牛产仔般
依然从我的肺中挠出一串欢笑，
我就不畏苹果，不惧洪流，
更不怕败血的春天。

男孩还是女孩？细胞问，
从肉身扔下一团梅子样的火。
假如我被孵化的毛发撩得心醉，
翼骨在脚后跟一阵阵发芽，
婴儿的腿窝挠得人发痒，
我就不畏绞架，不惧刀斧，
更不怕战火下交错的刀剑。

男孩还是女孩？手指问，
在墙上涂画绿衣少女和她的男人。
假如我被顽皮的饥渴撩得心醉，
预演的热流窜过神经元的边沿，
我就不畏爱的侵入，
不惧耻骨区的魔头，
更不怕直言不讳的坟墓。

① 诗人笔记本上标明这首诗写于 1934 年 4 月 30 日，1934 年 8 月首次发表于《新诗》。

狄兰·托马斯诗选

75

Dylan Thomas

If I were tickled by the lovers' rub

That wipes away not crow's-foot nor the lock

Of sick old manhood on the fallen jaws,

Time and the crabs and the sweethearting crib

Would leave me cold as butter for the flies,

The sea of scums could drown me as it broke

Dead on the sweethearts' toes.

This world is half the devil's and my own,

Daft with the drug that's smoking in a girl

And curling round the bud that forks her eye.

An old man's shank one-marrowed with my bone,

And all the herrings smelling in the sea,

I sit and watch the worm beneath my nail

Wearing the quick away.

And that's the rub, the only rub that tickles.

The knobbly ape that swings along his sex

From damp love-darkness and the nurse's twist

Can never raise the midnight of a chuckle,

Nor when he finds a beauty in the breast

Of lover, mother, lovers, or his six

Feet in the rubbing dust.

And what's the rub? Death's feather on the nerve?

Your mouth, my love, the thistle in the kiss?

My Jack of Christ born thorny on the tree?

假如我被恋人的抚爱撩得心醉，
却又抹不平额上乌鸦的足迹，
抹不去患病老人颔下的垂锁，
时光、蟹肿和情人的温床就会
留给我寒冷，如同黄油留给飞蝇，
沉渣浮动的大海就会淹没我，
海浪拍打爱人沉尸的脚趾。

这个世界半属魔鬼，半属我身，
愚蠢的女孩疯狂地吸毒
烟雾缠绕她眼上交错的花蕾。
老人的胫骨流动着与我相同的骨髓，
鲱鱼的气息弥漫整个大海，
我坐看指甲下的蠕虫
迅即消逝无踪。

这就是抚爱，撩人心醉的抚爱。
从湿润的爱的私处到护士的扭动
一脸疙瘩的莽汉摇曳一身的情欲
却永远无法撩拨午夜吃吃的笑语，
即便他发现了美，从恋人、母亲
和众情人的胸乳上，或从他
风尘撩动的六尺身躯。

抚爱是什么？是死亡的羽叶撩动着神经？
是你的嘴、我的爱亲吻中开放的蓟花？
是我的基督杰克毛茸茸地诞生在枝头？

The words of death are dryer than his stiff,
My wordy wounds are printed with your hair.
I would be tickled by the rub that is:
Man be my metaphor.

死亡的话语比他的僵尸更为干枯，
我喋喋不休的伤口印着你的毛发。
我愿被爱的抚摸撩得心醉，即
男人就是我的隐喻。

Our eunuch dreams

I

Our eunuch dreams, all seedless in the light,
Of light and love, the tempers of the heart,
Whack their boys' limbs,
And, winding-footed in their shawl and sheet,
Groom the dark brides, the widows of the night
Fold in their arms.

The shades of girls, all flavoured from their shrouds,
When sunlight goes are sundered from the worm,
The bones of men, the broken in their beds,
By midnight pulleys that unhouse the tomb.

II

In this our age the gunman and his moll,
Two one-dimensioned ghosts, love on a reel,
Strange to our solid eye,
And speak their midnight nothings as they swell;
When cameras shut they hurry to their hole
Down in the yard of day.

They dance between their arclamps and our skull,

我们的阉人梦见①

1

我们的阉人梦见光与爱，

光影中未留下种子，烦躁的心情

猛捶男孩的肢体，

他们裹着披肩和床单蜿蜒而行，

装扮黑暗中的新娘，黑夜的寡妇

搂在他们的怀里。

尸布的气味弥漫一切，姑娘的影子

随光线的西沉从蠕虫分离，

男人的身骨，在床笫衰败，

午夜的滑车掘开了坟墓。

2

在我们这个时代，杀手和他的情妇，

两个一丘之貉的鬼影，在胶片上做爱，

诉说子夜情欲高涨时的呓语，

在我们肉眼下尤为陌生；

当相机收起，他们就匆匆赶往

时光庭院里的窝穴。

他们手舞足蹈，在弧光灯和我们的颅骨间，

---

① 诗人笔记本上标明这首诗写于 1934 年 3 月，1934 年 4 月首次发表于
《新诗》。

Impose their shots, throwing the nights away;
We watch the show of shadows kiss or kill,
Flavoured of celluloid give love the lie.

III

Which is the world? Of our two sleepings, which
Shall fall awake when cures and their itch
Raise up this red-eyed earth?
Pack off the shapes of daylight and their starch,
The sunny gentlemen, the Welshing rich,
Or drive the night-geared forth.

The photograph is married to the eye,
Grafts on its bride one-sided skins of truth;
The dream has sucked the sleeper of his faith
That shrouded men might marrow as they fly.

IV

This is the world: the lying likeness of
Our strips of stuff that tatter as we move
Loving and being loth;
The dream that kicks the buried from their sack
And lets their trash be honoured as the quick.
This is the world. Have faith.

For we shall be a shouter like the cock,
Blowing the old dead back; our shots shall smack

强行拍摄，消磨夜晚的时光；
我们亲眼目睹影子们的亲吻或杀戮，
爱充满谎言，散发着赛璐珞^①的气味。

3

哪里是真实的世界？我们两人入睡，
谁会从梦中醒来，当药剂及痛痒
养育这红眼的世界？
快乐的绅士，威尔士的富人，
打发片片阳光和古板的风范，
或是挂上夜档前行。

相片嫁给了眼睛，
新娘植上真理的单面皮肤；
梦境吸走入眠人身上的信仰，
裹着尸布的男人或注入骨髓飞翔。

4

这就是世界：我们躺着
一样的衣衫褴褛，我们相爱
却又勉强如愿；
梦境将掩埋的尸体踢出眠床，
也让残骸像生者一样受人敬仰。
这就是世界。信心满满。

因为我们将像公鸡一样叫唤，
唤回昔日的死者；我们的拍摄将毁去

---

① 赛璐珞（celluloid），英语本义为明胶，可用来制作人造塑料，也可用来制作电影胶片。

The image from the plates;
And we shall be fit fellows for a life,
And who remain shall flower as they love,
Praise to our faring hearts.

碟中的影像；
我们将是顺应生活的伙伴，
活着的人们将开出爱的花朵，
颂扬我们远去的心。

Especially when the October wind

Especially when the October wind
With frosty fingers punishes my hair,
Caught by the crabbing sun I walk on fire
And cast a shadow crab upon the land,
By the sea's side, hearing the noise of birds,
Hearing the raven cough in winter sticks,
My busy heart who shudders as she talks
Sheds the syllabic blood and drains her words.

Shut, too, in a tower of words, I mark
On the horizon walking like the trees
The wordy shapes of women, and the rows
Of the star-gestured children in the park.
Some let me make you of the vowelled beeches,
Some of the oaken voices, from the roots
Of many a thorny shire tell you notes,
Some let me make you of the water's speeches.

Behind a pot of ferns the wagging clock
Tells me the hour's word, the neural meaning
Flies on the shafted disc, declaims the morning
And tells the windy weather in the cock.
Some let me make you of the meadow's signs;

Dylan Thomas 狄兰·托马斯诗选

尤其当十月的风^①

尤其当十月的风
伸出寒冷的手指痛击我的发丝，
受制于蟹行的太阳，我踏着烈火而来，
在地面投下一片影子，蟹一样爬行，
我站在海边，倾听群鸟的喧鸣，
倾听渡鸦咳叫在冬日的枝头，
我忙碌的心一阵阵颤栗，当她
倾泻音节般的血液，倾吐她的话语。

也被关入言词之塔，我留意
地平线上树林般行走的
女人身姿喋喋不休，以及公园里
一排排孩子星星般显露。
有人让我制作你，用发元音的山毛榉，
有人让我用橡树的声音，从荆棘丛生的
州郡根须告知你音符，
有人让我塑造你，用水的言词。

在一盆羊齿草后面，摇摆的钟
告诉我时辰的讯息，神经的意图
盘旋于茎秆的花盘，在雄鸡啼晓时，
宣告早晨降临，并预报刮风的天气。
有人让我制作你，用草地的标志；

① 1934 年 10 月 24 日首次发表于《倾听者》。

The signal grass that tells me all I know
Breaks with the wormy winter through the eye.
Some let me tell you of the raven's sins.

Especially when the October wind
(Some let me make you of autumnal spells,
The spider-tongued, and the loud hill of Wales)
With fist of turnips punishes the land,
Some let me make of you the heartless words.
The heart is drained that, spelling in the scurry
Of chemic blood, warned of the coming fury.
By the sea's side hear the dark-vowelled birds.

草符告诉我知晓的一切
透过目光挣脱蠕虫似的冬天。
有人让我告知你渡鸦的罪过。

尤其当十月的风
（有人让我塑造你，用秋天的字符，
蜘蛛的话语，以及威尔士喧闹的山岗）
握紧萝卜般的拳头惩处大地，
有人让我塑造你，用无情的词语。
心已耗尽，一股股疾奔的热血，
预警狂暴即刻来临。
站在海边，倾听群鸟鸣叫黑色的元音。

When, like a running grave

When, like a running grave, time tracks you down,
Your calm and cuddled is a scythe of hairs,
Love in her gear is slowly through the house,
Up naked stairs, a turtle in a hearse,
Hauled to the dome,

Comes, like a scissors stalking, tailor age,
Deliver me who, timid in my tribe,
Of love am barer than Cadaver's trap
Robbed of the foxy tongue, his footed tape
Of the bone inch,

Deliver me, my masters, head and heart,
Heart of Cadaver's candle waxes thin,
When blood, spade-handed, and the logic time
Drive children up like bruises to the thumb,
From maid and head,

For, sunday faced, with dusters in my glove,
Chaste and the chaser, man with the cockshut eye,
I, that time's jacket or the coat of ice
May fail to fasten with a virgin o
In the straight grave,

时光，像座奔跑的坟墓①

时光，像座奔跑的坟墓，一路追捕你，
你安然的拥抱是一把毛发的镰刀，
她换好挡，驾驭爱情缓缓穿过房室，
灵车里的乌龟，上了裸露的楼梯，
被拽向穹顶，

像一把剪刀，昂首阔步来裁剪岁月，
向部落中胆怯的我
传递比死亡陷阱更为外露的爱，
剥夺狡诈的口舌，他的带尺
丈量寸寸肉骨，

我的主人，传给我大脑和内心，
一颗蜡烛般消瘦的死亡之心，
当手铲之下的血和严密的时间
驱动孩子们成长，像青肿袭上拇指，
从少女及大脑，

因面对周日，手套里塞着抹布，
贞洁和猎手，男子的目光昏暗，
我，一身时令夹克或冰冷的外套，
也许无法和一位零形处女相守
僵直的墓穴，

① 写于 1934 年 11 月或 12 月初，专为收入《诗十八首》而作。

Stride through Cadaver's country in my force,
My pickbrain masters morsing on the stone
Despair of blood, faith in the maiden's slime,
Halt among eunuchs, and the nitric stain
On fork and face.

Time is a foolish fancy, time and fool.
No, no, you lover skull, descending hammer
Descends, my masters, on the entered honour.
You hero skull, Cadaver in the hangar
Tells the stick, 'fail.'

Joy is no knocking nation, sir and madam,
The cancer's fashion, or the summer feather
Lit on the cuddled tree, the cross of fever,
Not city tar and subway bored to foster
Man through macadam.

I damp the waxlights in your tower dome.
Joy is the knock of dust, Cadaver's shoot
Of bud of Adam through his boxy shift,
Love's twilit nation and the skull of state,
Sir, is your doom.

Everything ends, the tower ending and,
(Have with the house of wind), the leaning scene,
Ball of the foot depending from the sun,
(Give, summer, over), the cemented skin,
The actions' end.

我大步跨过死亡的国度，
我讨教的主人在石头上敲动密码，
血液绝望，可信的处女黏液，
在阉人间停留，裤裆和脸上
留下硝石的污迹。

时光是一种愚蠢的幻觉，时光与傻瓜。
不！不！情人的脑瓜，垂落的锤子
落下，我的主人，敲打获取的荣誉。
英雄的颅骨，机棚里的死尸
向手杖诉说"失败"。

快乐不是叮当作响的国度，先生和女士，
癌肿的风尚，或夏日的羽叶
在相拥的绿树和狂热十字架上闪亮，
城市的沥青和地铁不倦于养育
人类穿过碎石的小道。

我浇湿你圆形塔顶里的烛光。
快乐是尘埃的敲击，死尸穿越
盒内的突变，抽发亚当的芽胚，
爱情是暮色苍茫的国度及颅骨，
先生，全是你的劫数。

一切均已消亡，塔楼崩塌，
（风灌满空房），倾斜的布景，
足根从太阳悬落，
（夏天，到此为止），皮肤粘连，
所有的动作消亡。

All, men my madmen, the unwholesome wind
With whistler's cough contages, time on track
Shapes in a cinder death; love for his trick,
Happy Cadaver's hunger as you take
The kissproof world.

人啊，我疯狂的人，尽是腐败的风
传播吹哨者的咳嗽，追踪的时光
化为死亡的灰烬；爱上他的诡计，
快乐死尸饥肠辘辘，当你占据
这禁止亲吻的世界。

From love's first fever to her plague

From love's first fever to her plague, from the soft second
And to the hollow minute of the womb,
From the unfolding to the scissored caul,
The time for breast and the green apron age
When no mouth stirred about the hanging famine,
All world was one, one windy nothing,
My world was christened in a stream of milk.
And earth and sky were as one airy hill,
The sun and moon shed one white light.

From the first print of the unshodden foot, the lifting
Hand, the breaking of the hair,
And to the miracle of the first rounded word,
From the first secret of the heart, the warning ghost,
And to the first dumb wonder at the flesh,
The sun was red, the moon was grey,
The earth and sky were as two mountains meeting.

The body prospered, teeth in the marrowed gums,
The growing bones, the rumour of the manseed
Within the hallowed gland, blood blessed the heart,
And the four winds, that had long blown as one,

当初恋从狂热趋于烦扰①

当初恋从狂热趋于烦扰，当子宫
从柔软的瞬秒趋于空洞的分钟，
当胎膜随着一把剪子打开，
系上绿围裙哺乳的时光降临，
垂悬的饥荒周围没有嘴舌在骚动，
整个世界风雨过后，一片虚无，
我的世界在一条乳白的溪流里受洗。
大地和天空融为一处缥缈的山岗，
太阳和月亮洒下一样的白色光芒。

从赤足的第一行脚印，举起的手，
散乱的头发，
到首轮词语的非凡神奇，
从内心最初的秘密，预警的幽灵，
到第一次面对肉体时的默然惊愕，
太阳鲜红，月亮灰白，
大地和天空仿佛是两座山的相遇。

身体渐趋成熟，牙髓里长出牙齿，
骨骼在生长，神圣的腺体里
精液谣言般流窜，血液祝福心脏，
四面来风，始终如一地刮个不停，

① 诗人笔记本上标明这首诗写于 1933 年 10 月 14—17 日，1934 年 10 月
27—28 日首次发表于《准则》。

Shone in my ears the light of sound,
Called in my eyes the sound of light.
And yellow was the multiplying sand,
Each golden grain spat life into its fellow,
Green was the singing house.

The plum my mother picked matured slowly,
The boy she dropped from darkness at her side
Into the sided lap of light grew strong,
Was muscled, matted, wise to the crying thigh
And to the voice that, like a voice of hunger,
Itched in the noise of wind and sun.

And from the first declension of the flesh
I learnt man's tongue, to twist the shapes of thoughts
Into the stony idiom of the brain,
To shade and knit anew the patch of words
Left by the dead who, in their moonless acre,
Need no word's warmth.
The root of tongues ends in a spentout cancer,
That but a name, where maggots have their X.

I learnt the verbs of will, and had my secret;
The code of night tapped on my tongue;
What had been one was many sounding minded.

One womb, one mind, spewed out the matter,
One breast gave suck the fever's issue;
From the divorcing sky I learnt the double,

我的耳朵闪耀声音的光芒，
我的眼睛呼唤光芒的声音。
成倍增加的沙子一片金黄，
每一粒金沙繁衍成生命的伙伴，
颂唱的房子呈现绿意。

母亲采摘的梅子慢慢地成熟，
男孩从母体的黑暗中降生，
在明亮的膝下日趋健壮，
结实匀称，善于腿脚的啼哭，
善于发出声音，如饥饿的声音，
渴望风和太阳的喧闹。

从肉体的首次变格
我牙牙学语，学会将思想扭曲成
脑海里冷酷的词语，
重新修饰并编排前人遗留的
片言只语，在月光消逝的大地，
他们无需言语的温暖。
舌根在消耗殆尽的癌变中消亡，
空留虚名，只为蛆虫留下印迹。

我学会表达意愿的动词，拥有自己的秘密；
夜晚的密码轻叩我的舌面；
聚为一体的心智发出响亮不绝的声响。

一个子宫，一种思想，喷涌自身的内涵，
一只乳房触发吮吸的狂热；
从分离的天空，我学会了双重的涵义，

The two-framed globe that spun into a score;
A million minds gave suck to such a bud
As forks my eye;
Youth did condense; the tears of spring
Dissolved in summer and the hundred seasons;
One sun, one manna, warmed and fed.

双重的世界旋转为一次积分；
万千思想吮吸同一朵花蕾
犹如刀叉在眼前绽放；
青春无比浓郁；春的泪水
在夏天和成百的季节里消融；
一个太阳，一种甘露，带来温暖和养分。

In the beginning

In the beginning was the three-pointed star,
One smile of light across the empty face;
One bough of bone across the rooting air,
The substance forked that marrowed the first sun;
And, burning ciphers on the round of space,
Heaven and hell mixed as they spun.

In the beginning was the pale signature,
Three-syllabled and starry as the smile;
And after came the imprints on the water,
Stamp of the minted face upon the moon;
The blood that touched the crosstree and the grail
Touched the first cloud and left a sign.

In the beginning was the mounting fire
That set alight the weathers from a spark,
A three-eyed, red-eyed spark, blunt as a flower;
Life rose and spouted from the rolling seas,
Burst in the roots, pumped from the earth and rock
The secret oils that drive the grass.

In the beginning was the word, the word

最 初^①

最初是那三角的星星，
一丝光的微笑掠过空虚的脸；
一条骨的枝干穿越生根的空气，
物质分裂，构成太阳最初的精髓；
浑圆的天地燃烧着虚无，
天堂和地狱在旋转中混为一体。

最初是那苍白的署名，
三个音节，微笑般闪烁星光；
随后水面上出现印迹，
月亮显现铸造脸面的印痕；
触及桅顶横衍和圣杯的鲜血
触及最初的云彩，留下一丝痕迹。

最初是那上升的火苗，
一点星火点燃所有的天气，
三眼的星火，透出红光，迟钝如花；
生命萌发，自翻滚的大海喷涌而出，
从根须处迸发，渗自大地和岩石，
神秘的油催动青草成长。

最初是词语，那词语

① 诗人笔记本上标明这首诗写于1934年4月，更早的版本见于1933年9月，1934年12月发表于《诗十八首》。

That from the solid bases of the light
Abstracted all the letters of the void;
And from the cloudy bases of the breath
The word flowed up, translating to the heart
First characters of birth and death.

In the beginning was the secret brain.
The brain was celled and soldered in the thought
Before the pitch was forking to a sun;
Before the veins were shaking in their sieve,
Blood shot and scattered to the winds of light
The ribbed original of love.

源自光的坚实底座，
抽象成所有虚无的字母；
从呼吸那云雾缭绕的底座
词语不断涌现，向内心
传译生死最初的字符。

最初是那神秘的大脑。
脑细胞在思想中不断分裂衔接，
随后音叉迎着太阳分化；
在滤网震动血脉之前，
血液喷涌，迎着光束播撒
源初棱角分明的爱。

Light breaks where no sun shines

Light breaks where no sun shines;
Where no sea runs, the waters of the heart
Push in their tides;
And, broken ghosts with glow-worms in their heads,
The things of light
File through the flesh where no flesh decks the bones.

A candle in the thighs
Warms youth and seed and burns the seeds of age;
Where no seed stirs,
The fruit of man unwrinkles in the stars,
Bright as a fig;
Where no wax is, the candle shows its hairs.

Dawn breaks behind the eyes;
From poles of skull and toe the windy blood
Slides like a sea;
Nor fenced, nor staked, the gushers of the sky
Spout to the rod
Divining in a smile the oil of tears.

没有太阳照耀的地方，光降临[①]

没有太阳照耀的地方，光降临；
没有大海奔腾的地方，心潮掀起
自己的波涛；
而破碎的幽灵，一脑门的萤火虫，
光的万物
列队穿过肉体，那儿没有血肉装点身骨。

腿股间的烛火
温暖着青春和种子，点燃岁月的种子；
没有种子骚动的地方，
男人的果实，在星光下圆润光滑，
无花果一样明亮；
没有蜂蜡的地方，烛火映照它的毛发。

黎明在目光下破晓而出；
呼啸的热血，仿佛大海一样滑过
颅骨和脚趾的两极；
没有篱笆，没有树桩，天空下的喷井
朝着魔杖喷涌，
微笑中勘探泪水的原油。

狄兰·托马斯诗选

Dylan Thomas

107

---

① 诗人笔记本上标明这首诗写于 1933 年 11 月 20 日，1934 年 3 月 14 日
发表于《倾听者》时，改诗题为《光》。

Night in the sockets rounds,
Like some pitch moon, the limit of the globes;
Day lights the bone;
Where no cold is, the skinning gales unpin
The winter's robes;
The film of spring is hanging from the lids.

Light breaks on secret lots,
On tips of thought where thoughts smell in the rain;
When logics die,
The secret of the soil grows through the eye,
And blood jumps in the sun;
Above the waste allotments the dawn halts.

黑夜在眼窝里打转，

犹如黑漆漆的月亮，环绕地球的边界；

白昼照亮身骨；

没有严寒的地方，砭人肌骨的狂风

解开冬日的长袍；

春天的薄雾从眼睑上垂落。

光降临神秘的符签，

降临思维的末梢，那儿思想在雨中发霉；

随着逻辑消亡，

泥土的秘密透过目光而生长，

血液在阳光下高涨；

黎明逗留在荒芜的大地之上。

I fellowed sleep

I fellowed sleep who kissed me in the brain,
Let fall the tear of time; the sleeper's eye,
Shifting to light, turned on me like a moon.
So, 'planning-heeled, I flew along my man
And dropped on dreaming and the upward sky.

I fled the earth and, naked, climbed the weather,
Reaching a second ground far from the stars;
And there we wept, I and a ghostly other,
My mothers-eyed, upon the tops of trees;
I fled that ground as lightly as a feather.

'My fathers' globe knocks on its nave and sings.'
'This that we tread was, too, your father's land.'
'But this we tread bears the angelic gangs,
Sweet are their fathered faces in their wings.'
'These are but dreaming men. Breathe, and they fade.'

Faded my elbow ghost, the mothers-eyed,
As, blowing on the angels, I was lost
On that cloud coast to each grave-grabbing shade;
I blew the dreaming fellows to their bed

Dylan Thomas 狄兰·托马斯诗选

我与睡眠作伴^①

我与睡眠作伴，它在脑海亲吻我，
任岁月的泪水洒落；入睡的眼睛，
转向光，仿佛月亮一样开启我。
我因此调整脚跟，随着身姿飞翔，
坠入了梦境，飘向上浮的天空。

我逃离大地，赤裸着，攀上天气，
抵达远离群星的第二重地界；
我们哭泣，我及另一个幽魂，
我母性的目光，闪烁在树梢；
我逃离那重地界，羽毛般轻盈。

"我父辈的地球叩动它的轴心歌唱。"
"我们踩着的土地，也是你父辈的土地。"
"我们脚下的土地孕育成群的天使，
羽翼下那些慈父的脸庞多么亲切。"
"他们不过是些梦中人。吹口气，就会消失。"

消失，我肘边的幽魂，露出母性的目光，
正如我吹拂天使，迷失于
云岸，相连每一片攫取墓穴的阴影；
我将梦中的伙伴吹回到他们的眠床，

---

① 写于 1934 年 11 月或 12 月初，专为收入《诗十八首》而作。这首诗与
笔记本中写于 1933 年 10 月和 11 月的两首更早的诗相仿。

Where still they sleep unknowing of their ghost.

Then all the matter of the living air
Raised up a voice, and, climbing on the words,
I spelt my vision with a hand and hair,
How light the sleeping on this soily star,
How deep the waking in the worlded clouds.

There grows the hours' ladder to the sun,
Each rung a love or losing to the last,
The inches monkeyed by the blood of man.
An old, mad man still climbing in his ghost,
My fathers' ghost is climbing in the rain.

他们酣然沉睡，全然不知自己的幽魂。

随后空气中活着的万物
抬高了嗓音，而我攀上言词，
用手和毛发拼写自己的幻象，
入睡多么轻盈，在这污秽的星星
苏醒多么沉重，从那世俗的云层。

时光的阶梯向太阳生长，
每一级响彻爱或终将消逝，
寸寸跳动着男人的血液。
一位年迈疯子仍在攀缘他的阴魂，
我父辈的阴魂正在雨中攀缘。

I dreamed my genesis

I dreamed my genesis in sweat of sleep, breaking
Through the rotating shell, strong
As motor muscle on the drill, driving
Through vision and the girdered nerve.

From limbs that had the measure of the worm, shuffled
Off from the creasing flesh, filed
Through all the irons in the grass, metal
Of suns in the man-melting night.

Heir to the scalding veins that hold love's drop, costly
A creature in my bones I
Rounded my globe of heritage, journey
In bottom gear through night-geared man.

I dreamed my genesis and died again, shrapnel
Rammed in the marching heart, hole
In the stitched wound and clotted wind, muzzled
Death on the mouth that ate the gas.

Sharp in my second death I marked the hills, harvest
Of hemlock and the blades, rust
My blood upon the tempered dead, forcing

我梦见自身的起源[①]

一阵沉睡中的盗汗，我梦见自身的起源，
突破旋转的卵壳，壮如
钻头的运动肌，穿越
幻象和梁上的神经。

从蠕虫般丈量的肢体，从起皱的肉身，
曳步而落，锉过
草丛里的废铜烂铁，锉过
感人的夜晚那阳光般的金属。

承接流淌爱情热血的脉管，昂贵
是我骨骼中的生灵，
我环绕代代相传的地球，低速
驶过黑夜慢行的人类。

我梦见自身的起源，再次死去，榴弹
击中行进中的心脏，洞穿
缝合的伤口和凝结的风，死亡
堵住那张吞吃气体的嘴。

就在我再次死去，我标识了山岗，
丰收的毒芹和叶片，我的血
在僵硬的死尸上起了锈，迫使

① 写于 1934 年 11 月或 12 月初，专为收入《诗十八首》而作。

My second struggling from the grass.

And power was contagious in my birth, second
Rise of the skeleton and
Rerobing of the naked ghost. Manhood
Spat up from the resuffered pain.

I dreamed my genesis in sweat of death, fallen
Twice in the feeding sea, grown
Stale of Adam's brine until, vision
Of new man strength, I seek the sun.

我从草丛中再次奋发。

而我的诞生感染着力量，骨骼
再次生长，赤裸的
亡魂再次受劫。再次
受难的痛苦吐出男儿的气概。

一阵死亡的盗汗，我梦见自身的起源，
两度落入养育的大海，亚当的
汗水渐渐变质，直到梦见
强悍的新人，我去搜寻太阳。

All all and all the dry worlds lever

I

All all and all the dry worlds lever,
Stage of the ice, the solid ocean,
All from the oil, the pound of lava.
City of spring, the governed flower,
Turns in the earth that turns the ashen
Towns around on a wheel of fire.

How now my flesh, my naked fellow,
Dug of the sea, the glanded morrow,
Worm in the scalp, the staked and fallow.
All all and all, the corpse's lover,
Skinny as sin, the foaming marrow,
All of the flesh, the dry worlds lever.

II

Fear not the working world, my mortal,
Fear not the flat, synthetic blood,
Nor the heart in the ribbing metal.
Fear not the tread, the seeded milling,
The trigger and scythe, the bridal blade,
Nor the flint in the lover's mauling.

一切一切干枯的世界杠杆[①]

1

一切一切干枯的世界杠杆，

冰的舞台，坚实的海洋，

一切源于油，源于成磅的熔岩。

春天的城市，主宰的花朵，

在地球上转动，而地球环绕

一轮火球，转动灰白的城镇。

此刻怎样，我的肉身，赤裸的伙伴，

大海的乳房，腺体的未来，

颅内的蠕虫，木桩和休耕地。

一切的一切，僵尸的情人，

骨瘦如罪，流沫的骨髓，

一切的肉身，干枯的世界杠杆。

2

莫怕劳作的世界，我的凡胎，

莫怕平凡的人造血液，

更莫怕金属肋骨下的心脏。

不怕蹂躏，播种的碾磨，

不怕扳机和镰刀，新婚的刀锋，

更不怕情人间锤打的火石。

狄兰·托马斯诗选

119

Dylan Thomas

---

① 写于 1934 年 11 月或 12 月初，专为收入《诗十八首》而作。

Man of my flesh, the jawbone riven,
Know now the flesh's lock and vice,
And the cage for the scythe-eyed raven.
Know, O my bone, the jointed lever,
Fear not the screws that turn the voice,
And the face to the driven lover.

III

All all and all the dry worlds couple,
Ghost with her ghost, contagious man
With the womb of his shapeless people.
All that shapes from the caul and suckle,
Stroke of mechanical flesh on mine,
Square in these worlds the mortal circle.

Flower, flower the people's fusion,
O light in zenith, the coupled bud,
And the flame in the flesh's vision.
Out of the sea, the drive of oil,
Socket and grave, the brassy blood,
Flower, flower, all all and all.

我肉身的人类，撕裂的颌骨，
如今知晓肉身的锁闸和虎钳，
以及囚禁镰目乌鸦的鸟笼。
哦，我的身骨，焊接的杠杆，
莫怕转动声音的螺钉，
莫怕转向被逐情人的脸。

3

一切一切干枯的人间夫妻，
夫魂伴随妻魂，染病的人
伴随着孕育无形人的子宫。
一切成形于胎膜与乳液，
肉身机械地抚慰我身，
随着这凡俗的世界轮回。

人间的融合，花一样盛开，
哦，光芒四射，花蕾成对，
肉身的幻影火焰般升腾。
大海的深处，原油喷涌，
洞穴与墓穴，黄铜般的血液，
花朵，花朵，一切的一切。

This bread I break

This bread I break was once the oat,
This wine upon a foreign tree
Plunged in its fruit;
Man in the day or wind at night
Laid the crops low, broke the grape's joy.

Once in this wine the summer blood
Knocked in the flesh that decked the vine,
Once in this bread
The oat was merry in the wind;
Man broke the sun, pulled the wind down.

This flesh you break, this blood you let
Make desolation in the vein,
Were oat and grape
Born of the sensual root and sap;
My wine you drink, my bread you snap.

这片我切开的面包[①]

这片我切开的面包原是燕麦，
这杯酒原是一棵异国果树上
畅游的果汁；
白天的人，夜晚的风，
割倒一地的庄稼，捣碎葡萄的欢乐。

这酒中夏日的血
曾经叩动装饰藤蔓的果肉，
这面包里的燕麦
曾经在风中快乐地摇曳；
人击毁了太阳，摧垮了风。

你切开的肉质，你畅饮的血
在脉管中流动着忧伤，
燕麦和葡萄
原是天生肉感的根茎和液汁；
你畅饮我的美酒，你嚼食我的面包。

狄兰·托马斯诗选

Dylan Thomas

123

---

① 诗人笔记本上标明这首诗写于 1933 年 12 月 24 日，1936 年 7 月 16 日
　发表于《新英格兰周刊》。

Incarnate devil

Incarnate devil in a talking snake,
The central plains of Asia in his garden,
In shaping-time the circle stung awake,
In shapes of sin forked out the bearded apple,
And God walked there who was a fiddling warden
And played down pardon from the heavens' hill.

When we were strangers to the guided seas,
A handmade moon half holy in a cloud,
The wisemen tell me that the garden gods
Twined good and evil on an eastern tree;
And when the moon rose windily it was
Black as the beast and paler than the cross.

We in our Eden knew the secret guardian
In sacred waters that no frost could harden,
And in the mighty mornings of the earth;
Hell in a horn of sulphur and the cloven myth,
All heaven in a midnight of the sun,
A serpent fiddled in the shaping-time.

魔鬼化身^①

魔鬼化身为一条说话的蛇，
中亚平原伸缩在他的花园，
在成形的时光里，周期被蛰醒，
在原罪成形之际，叉出蓄胡的苹果，
上帝，失职的守护人，打那走过，
自天国的圣山贬下他的宽恕。

当我们陌生地面对牵引的大海，
一颗手工的月亮在云中略显神圣，
智者告诉我那花园的众神
在一株东方之树结出孪生的善恶，
当月亮在风中升起
野兽般黑暗，苍白甚过十字架。

我们在伊甸园结识秘密的守护神，
在寒霜无法冻结的圣水里，
在大地每一个强劲的早晨；
在硫黄号角和分裂神话的地狱，
在太阳子夜时分的整个天国，
一条蛇浪迹在成形的时光里。

① 1936 年 1 月 20 日定稿，更早的版本见于 1933 年 5 月 16 日。

狄兰·托马斯诗选

Dylan Thomas

125

The seed-at-zero

The seed-at-zero shall not storm
That town of ghosts, the trodden womb
With her rampart to his tapping,
No god-in-hero tumble down
Like a tower on the town
Dumbly and divinely stumbling
Over the manwaging line.

The seed-at-zero shall not storm
That town of ghosts, the manwaged womb
With her rampart to his tapping,
No god-in-hero tumble down
Like a tower on the town
Dumbly and divinely leaping
Over the warbearing line.

Through the rampart of the sky
Shall the star-flanked seed be riddled,
Manna for the rumbling ground,
Quickening for the riddled sea;
Settled on a virgin stronghold
He shall grapple with the guard
And the keeper of the key.

Dylan Thomas 狄兰·托马斯诗选

零度种子①

零度种子撼不垮
那座鬼城，遭人践踏的子宫
耸起她的壁垒抵挡他的叩击，
英雄之神绝不坍塌
像城中的一座高塔
默然而又神圣地绊倒
在人所发动的战线。

零度种子撼不垮
那座鬼城，历经战事的子宫
耸起她的壁垒抵挡他的叩击，
英雄之神绝不坍塌
像城中的一座高塔
默然而又神圣地越过
饱经战事的防线。

穿越天空的壁垒
星状侧翼种子将给出谜题，
甘露赐给隆隆的大地，
胎动波及谜一样的大海；
安顿在处女的堡垒，
他将扭打守卫
和钥匙的看守。

① 1936 年 9 月 10 日收入诗集《诗二十五首》。

Through the rampart of the sky
Shall the star-flanked seed be riddled,
Manna for the guarded ground,
Quickening for the virgin sea;
Settling on a riddled stronghold
He shall grapple with the guard
And the loser of the key.

May a humble village labour
And a continent deny?
A hemisphere may scold him
And a green inch be his bearer;
Let the hero seed find harbour,
Seaports by a drunken shore
Have their thirsty sailors hide him.

May a humble planet labour
And a continent deny?
A village green may scold him
And a high sphere be his bearer;
Let the hero seed find harbour,
Seaports by a thirsty shore
Have their drunken sailors hide him.

Man-in-seed, in seed-at-zero,
From the foreign fields of space,
Shall not thunder on the town
With a star-flanked garrison,
Nor the cannons of his kingdom

穿越天空的壁垒
星状侧翼种子将给出谜题，
甘露赐给防范的大地，
胎动波及处女海；
安居谜一样堡垒，
他将扭打守卫
和钥匙的失主。

卑微的村庄辛勤地劳作
大陆会不予认可吗？
整个半球也许对他责骂
绿色的英寸会是他的柩夫；
让英雄的种子找到港湾，
海港在沉醉的海岸上
让渴望的水手藏匿他的行踪。

卑微的行星辛勤地劳作
大陆会不予认可吗？
绿色的村庄也许对他责骂
高高的球体会是他的柩夫；
让英雄的种子找到港湾，
海港在渴望的海岸上
让沉醉的水手藏匿他的行踪。

播种的人，零度播种的人，
来自外层空间的域地，
他的星状侧翼军团
将打不垮那座城池，
他王国的炮火也不会

Shall the hero-in-tomorrow
Range on the sky-scraping place.

Man-in-seed, in seed-at-zero,
From the star-flanked fields of space,
Thunders on the foreign town
With a sand-bagged garrison,
Nor the cannons of his kingdom
Shall the hero-in-tomorrow
Range from the grave-groping place.

将明日的英雄
轰上摩天的高位。

播种的人，零度播种的人，
来自星状侧翼空间的域地，
背负沙袋的军团
轰炸异域的城池，
他王国的炮火也不会
将明日的英雄
轰出摸索墓穴的场所。

Shall gods be said to thump the clouds

Shall gods be said to thump the clouds
When clouds are cursed by thunder,
Be said to weep when weather howls?
Shall rainbows be their tunics' colour?

When it is rain where are the gods?
Shall it be said they sprinkle water
From garden cans, or free the floods?

Shall it be said that, venuswise,
An old god's dugs are pressed and pricked,
The wet night scolds me like a nurse?

It shall be said that gods are stone.
Shall a dropped stone drum on the ground,
Flung gravel chime? Let the stones speak
With tongues that talk all tongues.

据说众神将捶击云层①

据说众神将捶击云层，
当云彩遭受雷电的诅咒，
当天气怒吼，众神在抽泣？
彩虹将是他们锦袍的色彩？

当天上下雨时，众神在哪里？
据说他们将从花园的水罐里
喷洒出水雾，或让洪水奔流？

据说，维纳斯一样的
垂暮女神捏着扎着自己的瘪乳，
湿淋淋的夜晚像位护士训斥我？

据说众神都是石头。
一块陨石将擂响大地，
乐音砂石般飞扬？让石头说话
鼓动口舌演讲众多的语言。

① 诗人笔记本上标明这首诗写于 1933 年 7 月 17 日，后收入诗集《诗二十五首》时，略作删节。

狄兰·托马斯诗选

133

Dylan Thomas

Here in this spring

Here in this spring, stars float along the void;
Here in this ornamental winter
Down pelts the naked weather;
This summer buries a spring bird.

Symbols are selected from the years'
Slow rounding of four seasons' coasts,
In autumn teach three seasons' fires
And four birds' notes.

I should tell summer from the trees, the worms
Tell, if at all, the winter's storms
Or the funeral of the sun;
I should learn spring by the cuckooing,
And the slug should teach me destruction.

A worm tells summer better than the clock,
The slug's a living calendar of days;
What shall it tell me if a timeless insect
Says the world wears away?

在此春天①

在此春天，星星飘浮虚无的天际；
在此乔装的寒冬，
骤降赤裸的天气；
这个夏天掩埋一只春鸟。

象征符号选自岁月
缓缓地循环四季的海岸，
秋天讲授三个季节的篝火
和四只飞鸟的音符。

我该从树林辨识夏天，而蠕虫
竟能显露冬的风暴，
或太阳的葬礼；
我该从杜鹃声中感知春意，
而蛞蝓该教会我如何去毁灭。

蠕虫比时钟更能预报夏天，
蛞蝓是时光的活日历；
如果永恒的昆虫说世界消逝，
那它又向我预示什么？

① 诗人笔记本上标明这首诗写于 1933 年 7 月 9 日，后略作修订收于诗集《诗二十五首》。

狄兰·托马斯诗选

135

Dylan Thomas

Out of the sighs

Out of the sighs a little comes,
But not of grief, for I have knocked down that
Before the agony; the spirit grows,
Forgets, and cries;
A little comes, is tasted and found good;
All could not disappoint;
There must, be praised, some certainty,
If not of loving well, then not,
And that is true after perpetual defeat.

After such fighting as the weakest know,
There's more than dying;
Lose the great pains or stuff the wound,
He'll ache too long
Through no regret of leaving woman waiting
For her soldier stained with spilt words
That spill such acrid blood.

Were that enough, enough to ease the pain,
Feeling regret when this is wasted
That made me happy in the sun,
How much was happy while it lasted,

Dylan
Thomas
狄兰·托马斯诗选

136

叹息中①

叹息中流露出的点点滴滴，
可不是忧伤，因为在悲痛之前，
我按捺住哀伤；灵魂在生长
遗忘又哭闹；
流露出的点点滴滴，尝起来真好；
一切都不会失望；
谢天谢地，终究会存在某种必然，
假如爱得不够真，那便不是爱，
不断失败之后终成真。

一场弱小者熟知的战斗之后，
遗下的不止是死亡；
付出极度的痛苦或填平创伤，
他的痛太久太长，
无憾无悔地让一个女人等待
她的战士，沾染话语如溅，
溅出苦涩的血。

假如那足以、足以减轻痛苦，
耗尽痛苦又颇感遗憾，
令我沐浴阳光下的幸福，
那么后续的幸福又有多大，

狄兰·托马斯诗选

Dylan Thomas

137

---

① 诗人笔记本上标明这首诗写于 1932 年 6 月 7 日，后收入诗集《诗二十五首》。

Were vagueness enough and the sweet lies plenty,
The hollow words could bear all suffering
And cure me of ills.

Were that enough, bone, blood, and sinew,
The twisted brain, the fair-formed loin,
Groping for matter under the dog's plate,
Man should be cured of distemper.
For all there is to give I offer:
Crumbs, barn, and halter.

假如暧昧足矣，甜蜜的谎言足矣，
空洞的言语就能承受所有的苦难
并治愈我的伤痛。

假如那已足矣，骨骼、血液和肌腱，
扭曲的大脑、匀称的腰身，
狗碟之下进行的摸索，
人类就会治愈瘟疫。
这就是我所能奉献的一切：
面包屑、谷仓和牵狗绳。

Hold hard, these ancient minutes in the cuckoo's month

Hold hard, these ancient minutes in the cuckoo's month,
Under the lank, fourth folly on Glamorgan's hill,
As the green blooms ride upward, to the drive of time;
Time, in a folly's rider, like a county man
Over the vault of ridings with his hound at heel,
Drives forth my men, my children, from the hanging south.

Country, your sport is summer, and December's pools
By crane and water-tower by the seedy trees
Lie this fifth month unskated, and the birds have flown;
Holy hard, my country children in the world of tales,
The greenwood dying as the deer fall in their tracks,
The first and steepled season, to the summer's game.

And now the horns of England, in the sound of shape,
Summon your snowy horsemen, and the four-stringed hill,
Over the sea-gut loudening, sets a rock alive;
Hurdles and guns and railings, as the boulders heave,
Crack like a spring in a vice, bone breaking April,
Spill the lank folly's hunter and the hard-held hope.

等一等，布谷鸟月份中的古老时分①

等一等，布谷鸟月份中的古老时分，
在格拉摩根山②上第四道细长的栏杆下，
翠绿的花朵，随时光的催动，争相开放；
时间，化为愚蠢的骑手，像位乡间绅士
身后尾随着猎犬，奔驰在拱形的马道上，
自下悬的南方，驱赶我的人类，我的孩子。

乡村，你的运动是夏天，十二月的池塘
倚立着吊车，水塔倚立着多籽的树林，
五月尚未滑行，鸟儿却已飞翔；
等一等，我童话世界里的乡村小孩，
绿林奄奄一息，恰如鹿失陷自身的踪迹，
这最初的尖顶季节，适宜夏天的游戏。

此刻英格兰的号角，正吹响有形的声音，
召唤你雪中的骑手，而四弦的山岗
响彻海峡的上空，激活礁岩；
篱笆、枪支和栏杆，巨石般凸现，
像春天在邪恶中碎裂，骨骼敲碎四月，
倾泻瘦削愚蠢的猎手和难以驾驭的希望。

① 1936 年 3 月发表于《轻快帆船》。
② 格拉摩根山，位于诗人家乡斯旺西。

Down fall four padding weathers on the scarlet lands,
Stalking my children's faces with a tail of blood,
Time, in a rider rising, from the harnessed valley;
Hold hard, my county darlings, for a hawk descends,
Golden Glamorgan straightens, to the falling birds.
Your sport is summer as the spring runs angrily.

四种马蹄声声的天气落在猩红的土地，
拖着一尾血迹潜近孩子们的脸，
时间，化为骑手跃自马具般的山谷；
等一等，我乡间的宝贝，一只鹰飞落，
金色的格拉摩根山随坠落的鸟群挺直身姿。
你的运动是夏天，当春天愤然奔跑。

Was there a time

Was there a time when dancers with their fiddles
In children's circuses could stay their troubles?
There was a time they could cry over books,
But time has set its maggot on their track.
Under the arc of the sky they are unsafe.
What's never known is safest in this life.
Under the skysigns they who have no arms
Have cleanest hands, and, as the heartless ghost
Alone's unhurt, so the blind man sees best.

是否有过这样的时候①

是否有过这样的时候，在儿童乐园
他们伴琴声跳舞可解内心的烦忧？
曾经有过这样的时候，他们看书落泪，
时光却让蛆虫留意他们的踪迹。
苍穹荧光下，他们身处险境。
此生未知的一切最为安全。
空中广告牌下，失去臂膀的人
有双最干净的手，正如无情的幽灵
唯独不受伤害，盲人的眼看得最真切。

① 诗人笔记本上标明这首诗写于 1933 年 2 月 8 日，1936 年 7 月 30 日以
《诗篇》为题发表于《新英格兰周刊》。

Now

Now
Say nay,
Man dry man,
Dry lover mine
The deadrock base and blow the flowered anchor,
Should he, for centre sake, hop in the dust,
Forsake, the fool, the hardiness of anger.

Now
Say nay,
Sir no say,
Death to the yes,
The yes to death, the yesman and the answer,
Should he who split his children with a cure
Have brotherless his sister on the handsaw.

Now
Say nay,
No say sir
Yea the dead stir,
And this, nor this, is shade, the landed crow,
He lying low with ruin in his ear,
The cockerel's tide upcasting from the fire.

现　在①

现在
说不，
人，干枯的人，
我那干枯的情人
死礁般的基石，吹动开花的锚，
假如他在尘埃里围绕中心跳跃，
那么傻子，就会放弃持续的愤怒。

现在
说不，
先生说不，
向着是说死亡，
向着死亡说是，那是唯唯诺诺的回答，
假如他用药剂分解他的孩子，
那么手锯上的姐妹就会失去兄弟。

现在
说不，
先生说不
说是死者复苏，
阴影似是而非，乌鸦落地，
他躺在底下，耳内一片废墟，
好斗的小公鸡潮水般从火中升腾。

① 1936 年 9 月 10 日发表于《诗二十五首》。

狄兰·托马斯诗选

147

Dylan Thomas

Now

Say nay,

So star fall,

So the ball fail,

So solve the mystic sun, the wife of light,

The sun that leaps on petals through a nought,

The come-a-cropper rider of the flower.

Now

Say nay

A fig for

The seal of fire,

Death hairy-heeled, and the tapped ghost in wood,

We make me mystic as the arm of air,

The two-a-vein, the foreskin, and the cloud.

现在
说不，
星星随之陨落，
星球随之衰亡，
随之解决神秘的太阳，光的伴侣，
阳光透过虚无在花瓣上跳跃，
像一把修剪机骑上花丛。

现在
说不，
无花果
代表火漆，
死亡长出毛茸茸的后跟，叩击树林里的幽魂，
我们将我变得神秘，如同空中的手臂，
成双成对的血脉、包皮和云彩。

Why east wind chills

Why east wind chills and south wind cools
Shall not be known till windwell dries
And west's no longer drowned
In winds that bring the fruit and rind
Of many a hundred falls;
Why silk is soft and the stone wounds
The child shall question all his days,
Why night-time rain and the breast's blood
Both quench his thirst he'll have a black reply.

When cometh Jack Frost? the children ask.
Shall they clasp a comet in their fists?
Not till, from high and low, their dust
Sprinkles in children's eyes a long-last sleep
And dusk is crowded with the children's ghosts,
Shall a white answer echo from the rooftops.

All things are known: the stars' advice
Calls some content to travel with the winds,
Though what the stars ask as they round
Time upon time the towers of the skies
Is heard but little till the stars go out.

为何东风凛冽①

为何东风凛冽，南风送爽
要到风井干涸枯竭
西天不再沉溺于风中
才会知晓风成百上千次地
吹落秋天硬皮的果实；
为什么丝绸柔软，石头伤人
孩子会整天地询问，
为什么夜雨和乳血双双替他解渴，
而他却得到一个黑沉沉的回答。

杰克寒霜②何时降临？孩子们问。
他们的手心会否攥住彗星？
除非孩子们的尘埃，忽高忽低，
在他们的眼里撒下漫长的睡眠，
黄昏时分挤满孩子们的幽灵，
白色的回答才会在屋顶回荡。

万物皆可知：星星的建议
呼唤内涵与风同行，
尽管满天星斗的疑虑
不时地环绕天空之塔，
直到西沉才依稀可闻。

---

① 诗人笔记本上标明这首诗写于 1933 年 7 月 1 日，1936 年 7 月 16 日略
经修订发表于《新英格兰周刊》。
② 杰克寒霜（Jack Frost），即为严寒，一种拟人化的说法。

I hear content, and 'Be content'
Ring like a handbell through the corridors,
And 'Know no answer,' and I know
No answer to the children's cry
Of echo's answer and the man of frost
And ghostly comets over the raised fists.

我听到内涵，"满意"
仿佛摇响一只手铃穿过回廊，
"没有答案"，我知道
无法答复孩子们的乞求，
答复有关回声、寒霜之人以及
高举的拳头之上幽灵般的彗星。

A grief ago

A grief ago,
She who was who I hold, the fats and the flower,
Or, water-lammed, from the scythe-sided thorn,
Hell wind and sea,
A stem cementing, wrestled up the tower,
Rose maid and male,
Or, malted venus, through the paddler's bowl
Sailed up the sun;

Who is my grief,
A chrysalis unwrinkling on the iron,
Wrenched by my fingerman, the leaden bud
Shot through the leaf,
Was who was folded on the rod the aaron
Rose cast to plague,
The horn and ball of water on the frog
Housed in the side.

And she who lies,
Like exodus a chapter from the garden,
Brand of the lily's anger on her ring,
Tugged through the days

在悲伤之前[①]

在悲伤之前
她是我拥抱的人，脂肪与花朵，
或是，地狱风与大海，流水的鞭击，
源自镰刀状的荆棘，
一根梗茎凝结，攀缘塔尖而上，
少男少女起身
或是麦芽酿制的维纳斯，越过涉水者的碗形水域
启航驶向太阳；

谁是我的悲伤，
一只蝶蛹平俯于烙铁之上，
铅制的花蕾，为我的线人所振动，
射过枝叶绽放，
她是缠绕在艾伦魔杖[②]之上的
玫瑰撒向瘟疫，
号角和青蛙身上的水珠
在一侧垒窝。

她展身而卧，
像出埃及记章节离开花园，
她的戒指烙上百合的愤怒，
她祖先留下的绳索，

---

① 1935 年 10 月 23 日发表于《节目》。
② 艾伦魔杖（aaron's rod），据《圣经》中《出埃及记》章节，艾伦魔杖
　能创造奇迹，后化作蛇，又开出杏花并结果。

Her ropes of heritage, the wars of pardon,
On field and sand
The twelve triangles of the cherub wind
Engraving going.

Who then is she,
She holding me? The people's sea drives on her,
Drives out the father from the caesared camp;
The dens of shape
Shape all her whelps with the long voice of water,
That she I have,
The country-handed grave boxed into love,
Rise before dark.

The night is near,
A nitric shape that leaps her, time and acid;
I tell her this: before the suncock cast
Her bone to fire,
Let her inhale her dead, through seed and solid
Draw in their seas,
So cross her hand with their grave gipsy eyes,
And close her fist.

宽恕的战争，历经岁月的拖拉，
原野和沙滩之上
十二级三角形的天使之风
雕刻而逝。

那她是谁，
拥抱我的她是谁？人的海洋涌向她，
驱逐父亲离开独裁的营地；
有形的洞窟
用经久的水声塑造她的子孙，
我拥有她，
手垒的乡村墓穴围起了爱，
在天黑前升起。

夜色逼近，
硝的幽灵令她跃动，时间与酸；
我告诉她：在阳物点燃
她的骨头以前，
让她吸入她的尸体，透过种子和土地
汲取他们的大海，
所以她双手合十，眼中流露吉卜赛人的忧郁，
拳头紧握。

Ears in the turrets hear

Ears in the turrets hear
Hands grumble on the door,
Eyes in the gables see
The fingers at the locks.
Shall I unbolt or stay
Alone till the day I die
Unseen by stranger-eyes
In this white house?
Hands, hold you poison or grapes?

Beyond this island bound
By a thin sea of flesh
And a bone coast,
The land lies out of sound
And the hills out of mind.
No bird or flying fish
Disturbs this island's rest.

Ears in this island hear
The wind pass like a fire,
Eyes in this island see
Ships anchor off the bay.

耳朵在塔楼里听见[①]

耳朵在塔楼里听见
手在门上抱怨，
眼睛在山墙上看见
挂锁上的手指。
我打开门还是
独自隐居在白屋
不为陌生的眼睛看见
直到我死去的那一天？
手，拿的是毒药还是葡萄？

远在一片瘦弱的血肉之海
和骨岸环绕的
岛屿之外，
陆地静卧尘嚣之外，
丘陵淡出意念之外。
没有鸟儿或飞鱼
惊扰这片海岛的安宁。

耳朵在岛上听见
风像一团火掠过，
眼睛在岛上看见
船起锚驶离了港湾。

---

① 诗人笔记本上标明这首诗写于 1933 年 7 月 17 日，1934 年 5 月 5 日略
作删节发表于《伦敦约翰周刊》。

Shall I run to the ships
With the wind in my hair,
Or stay till the day I die
And welcome no sailor?
Ships, hold you poison or grapes?

Hands grumble on the door,
Ships anchor off the bay,
Rain beats the sand and slates.
Shall I let in the stranger,
Shall I welcome the sailor,
Or stay till the day I die?

Hands of the stranger and holds of the ships,
Hold you poison or grapes?

我是该奔向船队
让风撩起我的发梢，
还是逗留到死去的那一天
拒绝任何水手的光临？
船，载的是毒药还是葡萄？

手在门上抱怨，
船起锚驶离了港湾，
雨敲打沙砾和石板。
我该请进那位陌生人，
我该迎接那位水手，
还是逗留到死去的那一天？

陌生人的手，船队的货舱，
你们拿的是毒药还是葡萄？

The hand that signed the paper

The hand that signed the paper felled a city;
Five sovereign fingers taxed the breath,
Doubled the globe of dead and halved a country;
These five kings did a king to death.

The mighty hand leads to a sloping shoulder,
The finger joints are cramped with chalk;
A goose's quill has put an end to murder
That put an end to talk.

The hand that signed the treaty bred a fever,
And famine grew, and locusts came;
Great is the hand that holds dominion over
Man by a scribbled name.

The five kings count the dead but do not soften
The crusted wound nor stroke the brow;
A hand rules pity as a hand rules heaven;
Hands have no tears to flow.

那只签署文件的手[①]

那只签署文件的手毁灭了一座城市；
五根至高无上的手指扼住了呼吸，
死者的世界成倍扩大，国土又分成两半；
这五个王置一个王于死地。

那只强权的手伸向倾斜的臂膀，
手指的关节因钙化而痉挛；
一枝鹅毛笔结束了一场谋杀，
结束了一次谈话。

那只签署条约的手孕育一场热病；
饥荒蔓延，蝗虫四起；
伟大是那只统治人类的手，
签下一个潦草的名字。

这五个王清点死者，却不去抚慰
结痂的伤口，也不抚摸额头；
一只手统治怜悯，一只手统治天国；
两手无泪可流。

① 诗人笔记本上标明这首诗写于 1933 年 8 月 17 日，发表于《新诗》时省
去最后一节。

狄兰·托马斯诗选

163

Dylan Thomas

Should lanterns shine

Should lanterns shine, the holy face,
Caught in an octagon of unaccustomed light,
Would wither up, and any boy of love
Look twice before he fell from grace.
The features in their private dark
Are formed of flesh, but let the false day come
And from her lips the faded pigments fall,
The mummy cloths expose an ancient breast.

I have been told to reason by the heart,
But heart, like head, leads helplessly;
I have been told to reason by the pulse,
And, when it quickens, alter the actions' pace
Till field and roof lie level and the same
So fast I move defying time, the quiet gentleman
Whose beard wags in Egyptian wind.

I have heard many years of telling,
And many years should see some change.

The ball I threw while playing in the park
Has not yet reached the ground.

一旦灯笼闪亮①

一旦灯笼闪亮，圣洁的脸
落入异乎寻常的八角形灯光下，
迅然枯萎，而恋爱中的男孩
在失态前总会再度打量。
黑暗里他们隐秘的容颜
由血肉铸成，却任虚伪的日子降临。
消退的口红从她的双唇脱落，
干瘪的衣衫露出一只古老的乳房。

有人告诉我要用心来思考，
但心，仿佛大脑，引领着无望；
有人告诉我要用脉搏来思考。
而当脉搏加速，改变了行动的步伐，
田野和屋顶齐平无异，
我快速移动，抗拒着时光，这悠闲的绅士
他的胡须在埃及的风尘中飘摇。

多年来我一直听人诉说，
这么多年理应见到些变化。

我在公园玩耍时抛出的球
始终尚未落地。

① 1935 年 12 月发表于《新诗》，约写于 1933 年 3 月 1 日。

狄兰·托马斯诗选

165

Dylan Thomas

I have longed to move away

I have longed to move away
From the hissing of the spent lie
And the old terrors' continual cry
Growing more terrible as the day
Goes over the hill into the deep sea;
I have longed to move away
From the repetition of salutes,
For there are ghosts in the air
And ghostly echoes on paper,
And the thunder of calls and notes.

I have longed to move away but am afraid;
Some life, yet unspent, might explode
Out of the old lie burning on the ground,
And, crackling into the air, leave me half-blind.
Neither by night's ancient fear,
The parting of hat from hair,
Pursed lips at the receiver,
Shall I fall to death's feather.
By these I would not care to die,
Half convention and half lie.

我渴望远离①

我渴望远离
嘶嘶作响失效的谎言
以及持续恐怖的呼喊，
随着白昼翻越山岗坠入深海，
古老的恐惧之声愈演愈烈；
我渴望远离
不断重复的敬礼，
因为空中鬼影憧憧，
纸上幽灵般的回声不绝，
还有雷鸣般的呼喊和音符。

我渴望远离去，却又有些害怕，
尚未耗尽的生命，也许
会从地上燃烧的旧谎言中爆炸，
在空中劈啪作响，令我两眼昏花。
绝非因夜晚古老的恐惧，
帽子与头发分离，
因听筒旁噘起的嘴唇，
我会跌落到死亡的羽毛。
如果真是这样，我会不屑死去，
半是习俗，半是谎言。

① 诗人笔记本上标明这首诗写于 1933 年 3 月，1935 年 12 月首次发表于《新诗》，后略作修改收入诗集《诗二十五首》。

狄兰·托马斯诗选

167

Dylan Thomas

Grief thief of time

Grief thief of time crawls off,
The moon-drawn grave, with the seafaring years,
The knave of pain steals off
The sea-halved faith that blew time to his knees,
The old forget the cries,
Lean time on tide and times the wind stood rough,
Call back the castaways
Riding the sea light on a sunken path,
The old forget the grief,
Hack of the cough, the hanging albatross,
Cast back the bone of youth
And salt-eyed stumble bedward where she lies
Who tossed the high tide in a time of stories
And timelessly lies loving with the thief.

Now Jack my fathers let the time-faced crook,
Death flashing from his sleeve,
With swag of bubbles in a seedy sack
Sneak down the stallion grave,
Bull's-eye the outlaw through a eunuch crack
And free the twin-boxed grief,
No silver whistles chase him down the weeks'

悲伤的时光贼子①

悲伤的时光贼子缓缓地爬行，
　月亮牵引的坟墓，历尽海上漂泊的岁月，
辛劳的无赖偷走
大海分摊的信念，并将时光吹到膝下，
老人忘了哭喊，
时光斜倚潮头，风暴一次次狂啸，
呼唤海难者
在沉没的航道跃上大海的光芒，
老人忘了悲伤，
剧烈地咳嗽，信天翁在一旁盘旋，
追溯青春的骨骼，
两眼苦涩，跌落在她躺卧的床头，
她在一段故事里掀起浪涛，
无休无止地与那贼子做爱寻欢。

杰克，我的父辈，此刻放任时光面容的贼子，
他的袖口闪烁着死亡，
多籽的布袋装着抢夺来的泡沫，
潜入种马的坟墓，
睁开一双公牛的眼，穿过阉人的缝隙，
这歹徒释放双重囚禁的悲伤，
没有银亮的哨声追逐他，一周又一周，

① 写于 1935 年 8 月，尽管笔记本上更早的版本是 1933 年 8 月，1936 年 2 月 1 日首次发表于《彗星》。

狄兰·托马斯诗选

Dylan Thomas

169

Dayed peaks to day to death,
These stolen bubbles have the bites of snakes
And the undead eye-teeth,
No third eye probe into a rainbow's sex
That bridged the human halves,
All shall remain and on the graveward gulf
Shape with my fathers' thieves.

逼上日子的峰顶，逼近死亡，
这些失窃的泡沫留有蛇的牙痕
以及尖齿永久的印迹，
没有第三只眼睛窥探彩虹的性爱
在人类的两性间搭起桥梁，
一切残存在墓穴的深渊
铸成我父辈贼子的模样。

And death shall have no dominion

And death shall have no dominion.
Dead men naked they shall be one
With the man in the wind and the west moon;
When their bones are picked clean and the clean bones gone,
They shall have stars at elbow and foot;
Though they go mad they shall be sane,
Though they sink through the sea they shall rise again;
Though lovers be lost love shall not;
And death shall have no dominion.

And death shall have no dominion.
Under the windings of the sea
They lying long shall not die windily;
Twisting on racks when sinews give way,
Strapped to a wheel, yet they shall not break;
Faith in their hands shall snap in two,
And the unicorn evils run them through;
Split all ends up they shan't crack;
And death shall have no dominion.

And death shall have no dominion.
No more may gulls cry at their ears

而死亡也一统不了天下^①

而死亡也一统不了天下。
赤裸的死者一定会
与风中的人西天的月融为一体；
他们的骨头被剔净，白骨又消逝，
肘旁和脚下一定会有星星；
尽管发了疯，他们一定会清醒，
尽管沉落沧海，他们一定会再次升起；
尽管恋人会失去，爱却长存；
而死亡也一统不了天下。

而死亡也一统不了天下。
久卧在大海的旋涡之下，
他们决不会像风一样消逝；
即便在刑架上挣扎得筋疲力尽，
受缚于刑车之上，他们却一定不会碎裂；
信仰会在他们的手中折断，
独角兽的邪恶也一定会刺穿他们；
即便四分五裂，他们却不会崩溃；
而死亡也一统不了天下。

而死亡也一统不了天下。
海鸥不会再在他们耳边啼叫，

狄兰·托马斯诗选

Dylan Thomas

---

① 诗人笔记本上标明这首诗写于 1933 年 4 月，1933 年 5 月 18 日经修订
发表于《新英格兰周刊》。诗题出自于圣经《新约·罗马书》，指人若信
仰基督，肉体死，但灵魂永生。

Or waves break loud on the seashores;
Where blew a flower may a flower no more
Lift its head to the blows of the rain;
Though they be mad and dead as nails,
Heads of the characters hammer through daisies;
Break in the sun till the sun breaks down,
And death shall have no dominion.

波涛也不会再汹涌地拍打海岸；
花开花落之处也许不会再有花朵
迎着风雨而昂首挺立；
尽管他们发疯，钉子般僵死，
颇具个性的头颅却会从雏菊丛中崭露；
在阳光下碎裂，直到太阳陨落，
而死亡也一统不了天下。

Because the pleasure-bird whistles

Because the pleasure-bird whistles after the hot wires,

Shall the blind horse sing sweeter?

Convenient bird and beast lie lodged to suffer

The supper and knives of a mood.

In the sniffed and poured snow on the tip of the tongue of the year

That clouts the spittle like bubbles with broken rooms,

An enamoured man alone by the twigs of his eyes, two fires,

Camped in the drug-white shower of nerves and food,

Savours the lick of the times through a deadly wood of hair

In a wind that plucked a goose,

Nor ever, as the wild tongue breaks its tombs,

Rounds to look at the red, wagged root.

Because there stands, one story out of the bum city,

That frozen wife whose juices drift like a fixed sea

Secretly in statuary,

Shall I, struck on the hot and rocking street,

Not spin to stare at an old year

Toppling and burning in the muddle of towers and galleries

Like the mauled pictures of boys?

The salt person and blasted place

I furnish with the meat of a fable;

因为快乐鸟嗯哨[①]

因为快乐鸟随热线嗯哨，
瞎马是否会叫得更欢畅？
就近栖居的鸟兽忍受住晚餐和刀叉
同样心境下的切割。
在岁月的舌尖上抽吸疾唾的雪花
像破碎的泡沫轻轻叩击唾液，
一位迷恋的人，眼神犹如两团火苗闪烁，
神经和食物白药般倾泻他独自露营的身影，
饱尝乱发般的死树林一次次地舔舐
狂风漫卷的鹅毛大雪，
而当狂野的舌头摧毁它的坟墓，
他也不会环顾红色松动的根。
因为妻子站在那儿，一个废城的故事，
冻结的体液像凝固的大海
在雕像里悄然漂浮，
我敲击热烘烘摇晃的街道，
是否不该回眸旧岁，
像那幅受损的男孩画像倾覆燃烧
在混乱的塔楼和画廊？
盐人及其被毁的场所
我供给虚构的肉食；

---

① 1939 年 2 月首次发表于《二十世纪诗歌》。

If the dead starve, their stomachs turn to tumble
An upright man in the antipodes
Or spray-based and rock-chested sea:
Over the past table I repeat this present grace.

如果死者挨饿，他们的胃
就会掀翻反向直立的人，
或许搅翻浪花四溅暗礁丛生的大海：
在往日的餐桌上我重复此刻的优雅。

When all my five and country senses see

When all my five and country senses see,
The fingers will forget green thumbs and mark
How, through the halfmoon's vegetable eye,
Husk of young stars and handfull zodiac,
Love in the frost is pared and wintered by,
The whispering ears will watch love drummed away
Down breeze and shell to a discordant beach,
And, lashed to syllables, the lynx tongue cry
That her fond wounds are mended bitterly.
My nostrils see her breath burn like a bush.

My one and noble heart has witnesses
In all love's countries, that will grope awake;
And when blind sleep drops on the spying senses,
The heart is sensual, though five eyes break.

当我天生的五官看见[①]

当我天生的五官看见，
手指将忘却嫩绿的拇指
透过半月形的植物眼，留意
新星的外壳和黄道十二宫的运行，
霜冻中的爱如何被修剪过冬，
低语的耳朵将目送爱随鼓声远去，
沿着微风和贝壳飘向不谐的海滩，
山猫般灵活的口舌抽动音节呼喊，
她钟爱的伤口痛苦地愈合。
我的鼻孔看见她的呼吸灌木般燃烧。

我一颗高贵的心在爱的国度
留有见证，他们将摸索着醒来；
当失明的睡眠降临于窥视的感官，
心依然有情，尽管五眼已毁。

---

① 1938 年 8 月首次发表于《诗歌》（芝加哥）。

We lying by seasand

We lying by seasand, watching yellow
And the grave sea, mock who deride
Who follow the red rivers, hollow
Alcove of words out of cicada shade,
For in this yellow grave of sand and sea
A calling for colour calls with the wind
That's grave and gay as grave and sea
Sleeping on either hand.
The lunar silences, the silent tide
Lapping the still canals, the dry tide-master
Ribbed between desert and water storm,
Should cure our ills of the water
With a one-coloured calm;
The heavenly music over the sand
Sounds with the grains as they hurry
Hiding the golden mountains and mansions
Of the grave, gay, seaside land.
Bound by a sovereign strip, we lie,
Watch yellow, wish for wind to blow away
The strata of the shore and drown red rock;
But wishes breed not, neither
Can we fend off rock arrival,
Lie watching yellow until the golden weather
Breaks, O my heart's blood, like a heart and hill.

我们躺在沙滩上①

我们躺在沙滩上，眺望黄色
而凝重的大海，嘲笑那些嘲笑者，
那些随红河而下的人，蝉影下
我们掏空所有的话语，
这黄色而凝重的大海和沙滩
随风响起渴望色彩的呼唤，

坟墓般凝重，大海般欢乐，
沉睡在任何一条手臂上。
月色宁静，潮水默然
轻拍静静的运河，干燥的潮闸
横守在沙漠和洪水间，
单色的沉静理应治愈
我们的水患；

沙滩上天堂般的乐音
响起，随飞沙急切地隐匿
凝重而欢快的海滨之上
金色的山峦和大厦。
身为无上的沙滩所系，我们
仰卧眺望黄色的大海，渴望风
刮走层层海岸，溺死赤色的礁石；
但是情非所愿，我们
无法阻挡礁石的到来，
我们仰卧眺望黄色的大海，直到金色的天气
破碎。哦，我的心在流血，仿佛心，仿佛山峦。

① 诗人笔记本上标明这首诗写于 1933 年 5 月 16 日，1937 年 1 月经修订
后发表于《诗歌》（芝加哥）。

狄兰·托马斯诗选

Dylan Thomas

183

It is the sinners' dust-tongued bell

It is the sinners' dust-tongued bell claps me to churches
When, with his torch and hourglass, like a sulphur priest,
His beast heel cleft in a sandal,
Time marks a black aisle kindle from the brand of ashes,
Grief with dishevelled hands tear out the altar ghost
And a firewind kill the candle.

Over the choir minute I hear the hour chant:
Time's coral saint and the salt grief drown a foul sepulchre
And a whirlpool drives the prayerwheel;
Moonfall and sailing emperor, pale as their tideprint,
Hear by death's accident the clocked and dashed-down spire
Strike the sea hour through bellmetal.

There is loud and dark directly under the dumb flame,
Storm, snow, and fountain in the weather of fireworks,
Cathedral calm in the pulled house;
Grief with drenched book and candle christens the cherub time
From the emerald, still bell; and from the pacing weather-cock
The voice of bird on coral prays.

Forever it is a white child in the dark-skinned summer
Out of the font of bone and plants at that stone tocsin

是罪人的尘埃之舌鼓动起钟声^①

是罪人的尘埃之舌鼓动起钟声轻拍我走向教堂，
此刻带着火把和沙漏，像一位满身硫黄味的牧师，
他走兽般的脚跟在凉鞋里爆裂，
时光流痕，烙下的余烬点燃黑色的走廊，
悲伤伸出凌乱的双手撕碎这祭坛上的幽灵，
而一阵风卷起火焰扑灭烛光。

在合唱圣诗的时刻，我听到时间的诵唱：
时光珊瑚般的圣徒和咸涩的悲伤淹没污秽的坟墓，
一股旋涡推动着祈祷轮；
月落和航海的帝王，苍白如潮水的流痕，
死亡的灾难旁，我听到俯冲而下的报时钟声
透过塔顶的大钟敲响大海的时光。

无声的火焰下方，一阵喧嚣一片黑暗，
烟火般的天气夹杂着风暴、飞雪和喷泉般的暴雨，
拔地而起的房屋教堂般宁静；
悲伤翻阅湿淋淋的圣书，烛光洗礼天使的时光，
伴随一阵翠绿而宁静的钟声；而在风向标的缓缓转动中
鸟儿在珊瑚丛发出声声祈祷。

在黑皮肤的夏天，孩子永远是那么洁白无瑕，
在石头的警报声中，从动植物的圣水池

---

① 首次发表于 1937 年《二十世纪诗歌》。

Scales the blue wall of spirits;
From blank and leaking winter sails the child in colour,
Shakes, in crabbed burial shawl, by sorcerer's insect woken,
Ding dong from the mute turrets.

I mean by time the cast and curfew rascal of our marriage,
At nightbreak born in the fat side, from an animal bed
In a holy room in a wave;
And all love's sinners in sweet cloth kneel to a hyleg image,
Nutmeg, civet, and sea-parsley serve the plagued groom and bride
Who have brought forth the urchin grief.

攀缘灵魂蓝色的房墙；

身着彩衣的孩子驶出渗漏又空茫的冬天，

在巫师唤醒的蠕虫旁，斜披乖张的头巾，

将沉默的塔楼摇得叮咚作响。

我说在晚钟萦绕的黄昏，在波涛汹涌的圣屋里

婚姻的小淘气从肥肥的身躯降生

在一张兽性的大床；

此刻，爱情所有的罪人身着盛装去跪拜原初的圣像，

豆蔻、麝猫和海欧芹供奉染上瘟疫的新郎新娘，

顽童的悲伤就此降生。

O make me a mask

O make me a mask and a wall to shut from your spies
Of the sharp, enamelled eyes and the spectacled claws
Rape and rebellion in the nurseries of my face,
Gag of dumbstruck tree to block from bare enemies
The bayonet tongue in this undefended prayerpiece,
The present mouth, and the sweetly blown trumpet of lies,
Shaped in old armour and oak the countenance of a dunce
To shield the glistening brain and blunt the examiners,
And a tear-stained widower grief drooped from the lashes
To veil belladonna and let the dry eyes perceive
Others betray the lamenting lies of their losses
By the curve of the nude mouth or the laugh up the sleeve.

Dylan Thomas 狄兰·托马斯诗选

哦，为我打制一副面具①

哦，为我打制一副面具，砌起一面墙挡住你
那双珐琅质锐眼的窥探以及那戴眼镜的利爪
在我苗圃般的脸面上为所欲为，
用目瞪口呆的树木打制口嚼，挡开赤裸裸的敌手
挡开这篇毫不防卫的祷文里刺刀般的口舌，
眼前这张嘴，喇叭一样鼓动甜蜜的谎言，
套上古老的盔甲和橡木，打造傻瓜的尊容，
遮掩闪光的大脑，钝化检查官的感官，
泪迹斑斑的鳏夫从眼睫垂落悲伤
掩饰颠茄，让哭干的眼睛察觉
旁人凭裸嘴的曲线或袖子的私笑
出卖他们悲悯自身失败的谎言。

狄兰·托马斯诗选

189

Dylan Thomas

---

① 诗人笔记本上标明这首诗最早写于 1933 年 2 月，1938 年 8 月经修订首次发表于《诗歌》(芝加哥)。

The spire cranes

The spire cranes. Its statue is an aviary.
From the stone nest it does not let the feathery
Carved birds blunt their striking throats on the salt gravel,
Pierce the spilt sky with diving wing in weed and heel
An inch in froth. Chimes cheat the prison spire, pelter
In time like outlaw rains on that priest, water,
Time for the swimmers' hands, music for silver lock
And mouth. Both note and plume plunge from the spire's hook.
Those craning birds are choice for you, songs that jump back
To the built voice, or fly with winter to the bells,
But do not travel down dumb wind like prodigals.

塔尖，鹤一样耸立①

塔尖，鹤一样耸立。一座鸟笼的雕像。
自石砌的巢穴处，它就不让羽毛柔软的
石刻小鸟，在咸涩的沙砾上磨钝它们尖脆的嗓音，
刺穿四溅的天空，俯冲的翅翼插入水草丛，
后爪浅涉浮沫。钟声骗过监狱的塔尖，
像囚犯时而骤降一阵雨到神甫身上，
流水、时光拍打游泳者的手，乐音飘向
银锁和河口。音符和羽毛双双自塔尖的尽头飘落。
那些鹤一样的鸟儿任你挑选，歌声跃回到
成型的嗓音，或随冬天一起飞向钟声，
却不像浪子，随暗哑的风一路漂泊。

---

① 这首诗最早写于 1931 年 1 月 27 日的笔记本中，1938 年正式发表时作
了较大的修订。

After the funeral

(In memory of Ann Jones)

After the funeral, mule praises, brays,
Windshake of sailshaped ears, muffle-toed tap
Tap happily of one peg in the thick
Grave's foot, blinds down the lids, the teeth in black,
The spittled eyes, the salt ponds in the sleeves,
Morning smack of the spade that wakes up sleep,
Shakes a desolate boy who slits his throat
In the dark of the coffin and sheds dry leaves,
That breaks one bone to light with a judgment clout,
After the feast of tear-stuffed time and thistles
In a room with a stuffed fox and a stale fern,
I stand, for this memorial's sake, alone
In the snivelling hours with dead, humped Ann
Whose hooded, fountain heart once fell in puddles
Round the parched worlds of Wales and drowned each sun
(Though this for her is a monstrous image blindly
Magnified out of praise; her death was a still drop;
She would not have me sinking in the holy
Flood of her heart's fame; she would lie dumb and deep
And need no druid of her broken body).

葬礼之后①

（纪念安·琼斯）

葬礼之后，骡子哞哞地赞美，
风扇动帆形的双耳，裹紧的蹄子
在厚实的坟基轻快地叩击
一根木桩，眼帘垂闭，牙齿又发黑，
眼里冒出唾液，袖口流成盐池，
早晨铁锹惊醒睡梦的铲击声，
惊动一个孤独的男孩，他在漆黑的
棺材里，撕开了喉咙，褪落枯叶，
最后的一击让一根白骨暴殄，
饱尝泪水盈盈的时光盛宴和紫蓟后
狐狸在房内暴食，羊齿草发臭，
我独自站立，为了心中这一份悼念，
在此饮泣的时刻陪伴死者，驼了背的安，
她遮裹的心泉，汇成干裂的威尔士旷野
四周的水坑，溺死每一颗太阳，
（尽管这对她而言只是一个怪异的形象，赞美
过于盲目；她的死原是一次宁静的水滴；
她并不希望我沉溺于她的善心及其名声
所引发的圣潮，她愿默默地安息，
不必为她破碎的身子祈祷）。

狄兰·托马斯诗选

Dylan Thomas

193

① 诗人笔记本上标明这首诗写于1933年2月10日，诗人姨妈安·琼斯（Ann Jones）去世那一天，后作了大幅度的修改，1938年夏首次发表于《今日生活与书信》。安·琼斯居住在羊齿山农庄，享年70岁。

But I, Ann's bard on a raised hearth, call all
The seas to service that her wood-tongued virtue
Babble like a bellbuoy over the hymning heads,
Bow down the walls of the ferned and foxy woods
That her love sing and swing through a brown chapel,
Bless her bent spirit with four, crossing birds.
Her flesh was meek as milk, but this skyward statue
With the wild breast and blessed and giant skull
Is carved from her in a room with a wet window
In a fiercely mourning house in a crooked year.
I know her scrubbed and sour humble hands
Lie with religion in their cramp, her threadbare
Whisper in a damp word, her wits drilled hollow,
Her fist of a face died clenched on a round pain;
And sculptured Ann is seventy years of stone.
These cloud-sopped, marble hands, this monumental
Argument of the hewn voice, gesture and psalm,
Storm me forever over her grave until
The stuffed lung of the fox twitch and cry Love
And the strutting fern lay seeds on the black sill.

而我，安的吟游诗人，立于壁炉的高台之上，
呼唤所有的大海为她歌唱，她缄默的美德
像浮标铃一样在颂扬者的头上喋喋不休，
弯下围墙般的羊齿草和狡猾的树林
让她爱的歌声飘荡，穿过褐色的教堂，
四只穿梭的鸟祝福她俯服的灵魂。
她的肌肤牛奶一样温顺，而这高耸的雕像
挺起狂野的胸乳，扬起神圣而巨大的头骨，
塑自她的原型，雕成于那窗口透着潮气，
佝偻岁月里一间深切悼念的房室。
我知道她那双洁净、酸痛而谦卑的手
仍然紧握着她的信仰，潮湿的话语
倾诉如旧，她的心智渐渐干涸，
拳头般紧绷的脸抓紧圆形的痛苦而去；
安的雕像是位七旬的老人。
一双浸透云雾的大理石手，这些表达不朽而
精心打磨的声音、姿势和圣歌
永远在她的坟头震撼着我
直到狐狸暴食的肺腑抽搐，呼喊爱情，
昂首阔步的羊齿草在黑色的窗台播下种子。

Once it was the colour of saying

Once it was the colour of saying
Soaked my table the uglier side of a hill
With a capsized field where a school sat still
And a black and white patch of girls grew playing;
The gentle seaslides of saying I must undo
That all the charmingly drowned arise to cockcrow and kill.
When I whistled with mitching boys through a reservoir park
Where at night we stoned the cold and cuckoo
Lovers in the dirt of their leafy beds,
The shade of their trees was a word of many shades
And a lamp of lightning for the poor in the dark;
Now my saying shall be my undoing,
And every stone I wind off like a reel.

Dylan Thomas 狄兰·托马斯诗选

那话语的音色曾经①

那话语的音色曾经
浸透我的书桌，山峦更险恶的一侧，
一所宁静的学校坐落在倾覆的田野，
满地黑白相间的少女在嬉闹中成长；
我必须掀开大海滑行般的话语，
让所有迷人的溺水者在黎明升腾相互残杀。
当我和逃学的男孩吹着口哨走过水库公园，
在夜晚我们朝布谷鸟般絮语的恋人抛掷石块，
他们哆哆嗦嗦地躺在松土和落叶的眠床，
他们的树影是许多影子的言词，
而闪电的明灯照亮黑暗中的穷人；
此刻我的话语将开启我的毁灭，
我像解开线轴一样解开每块石子。

狄兰·托马斯诗选

Dylan Thomas

_____

① 1939 年 3 月首次发表于《威尔士》。

Not from this anger

Not from this anger, anticlimax after
Refusal struck her loin and the lame flower
Bent like a beast to lap the singular floods
In a land strapped by hunger
Shall she receive a bellyful of weeds
And bear those tendril hands I touch across
The agonized, two seas.

Behind my head a square of sky sags over
The circular smile tossed from lover to lover
And the golden ball spins out of the skies;
Not from this anger after
Refusal struck like a bell under water
Shall her smile breed that mouth, behind the mirror,
That burns along my eyes.

并非因这种愤怒①

并非因这种愤怒，遭拒后的
低潮击中她的耻骨区，残废的花朵
像一头垂首的野兽，舔着独特的洪潮
在一片饥渴围困的土地，
她会承接满腹的杂草，
承受我触及的那双卷须般的手
拂过两片痛苦的海洋。

一方天空在我脑后垂落，
微笑在恋人间循环地摇荡，
而金色的圆球旋出天空；
并非因遭拒后的愤怒，
仿佛钟声在水下敲响，
她的微笑会养育那张嘴，在镜子后，
沿着我的眼睛燃烧。

---

① 诗人笔记本上标明这首诗写于 1933 年 4 月 20 日，1938 年 8 月经大幅
度缩减修订后发表于《诗歌》(芝加哥)。

The tombstone told when she died

The tombstone told when she died.
Her two surnames stopped me still.
A virgin married at rest.
She married in this pouring place,
That I struck one day by luck,
Before I heard in my mother's side
Or saw in the looking-glass shell
The rain through her cold heart speak
And the sun killed in her face.
More the thick stone cannot tell.

Before she lay on a stranger's bed
With a hand plunged through her hair,
Or that rainy tongue beat back
Through the devilish years and innocent deaths
To the room of a secret child,
Among men later I heard it said
She cried her white-dressed limbs were bare
And her red lips were kissed black,
She wept in her pain and made mouths,
Talked and tore though her eyes smiled.

I who saw in a hurried film

她死后的墓碑在诉说[①]

她死后的墓碑在诉说。
她的双姓让我默然止步。
一位处女成婚于长眠。
她在此大雨滂沱里成婚，
我也是一天碰巧路过，
后从母亲那儿听说了，
或许从穿衣镜外壳上看到
雨水透过她冰冷的心诉说
阳光在她的脸面惨遭杀戮。
沉重的碑石说不出更多。

她曾躺在陌生人的床上，
一只手拢起头发，
或是那雨水般的口舌
穿越邪恶的年代和无邪的死亡，
不断提及私生子的房室，
后来我听许多人说起，
她裸着白皙的四肢哭喊，
鲜红的嘴唇被吻得发黑，
她痛苦地流泪，嘴角抽泣着
倾诉，尽管眼神依然在微笑。

我在一部短片里看到

狄兰·托马斯诗选

Dylan Thomas

---

① 1938 年冬首次发表于《七》。

Death and this mad heroine

Meet once on a mortal wall

Heard her speak through the chipped beak

Of the stone bird guarding her:

I died before bedtime came

But my womb was bellowing

And I felt with my bare fall

A blazing red harsh head tear up

And the dear floods of his hair.

死亡并与发疯的女主角
一度相逢于世俗的墙垣
听到她借助守卫鸟
那张破损的石嘴诉说：
我在就寝前就已死去
但我的子宫仍在咆哮
我感到裸露的身子在下坠
赤焰般刺耳的头颅摧毁一切
他可爱的毛发喷涌而出。

On no work of words

On no work of words now for three lean months in the bloody
Belly of the rich year and the big purse of my body
I bitterly take to task my poverty and craft:

To take to give is all, return what is hungrily given
Puffing the pounds of manna up through the dew to heaven,
The lovely gift of the gab bangs back on a blind shaft.

To lift to leave from the treasures of man is pleasing death
That will rake at last all currencies of the marked breath
And count the taken, forsaken mysteries in a bad dark.

To surrender now is to pay the expensive ogre twice.
Ancient woods of my blood, dash down to the nut of the seas
If I take to burn or return this world which is each man's work.

当词语失效①

当词语失效，我苦苦地申斥自身的贫乏和技艺，
我身体的大皮囊和丰年流血的饥腹
此刻已歉收了三个月：

奉献已尽，回赠饥饿时获取的一切
吹送缕缕成磅的甘露穿越露珠抵达天堂，
话语动人的天赋回撞盲目的箭杆。

起身离别人类的宝藏是令人愉悦的死亡
最终将搜寻所有清新流动的呼吸
清点黑暗深处攫取并废弃的神秘。

此刻屈服是向奢华的恶魔付出双倍的代价。
假如我要焚毁或复归这个世界，即世人的使命，
我热血滋养的远古森林，顺流冲击大海的坚果。

狄兰·托马斯诗选

Dylan Thomas

205

① 1939 年 3 月首次发表于《威尔士》。

'If my head hurt a hair's foot'

'If my head hurt a hair's foot
Pack back the downed bone. If the unpricked ball of my breath
Bump on a spout let the bubbles jump out.
Sooner drop with the worm of the ropes round my throat
Than bully ill love in the clouted scene.

'All game phrases fit your ring of a cockfight:
I'll comb the snared woods with a glove on a lamp,
Peck, sprint, dance on fountains and duck time
Before I rush in a crouch the ghost with a hammer, air,
Strike light, and bloody a loud room.

'If my bunched, monkey coming is cruel
Rage me back to the making house. My hand unravel
When you sew the deep door. The bed is a cross place.
Bend, if my journey ache, direction like an arc or make
A limp and riderless shape to leap nine thinning months.'

'No. Not for Christ's dazzling bed
Or a nacreous sleep among soft particles and charms
My dear would I change my tears or your iron head.
Thrust, my daughter or son, to escape, there is none, none, none,
Nor when all ponderous heaven's host of waters breaks.

"如果我的头伤着一丝发根"①

"如果我的头伤着一丝发根
那就包好毛茸茸的骨骼。如果我未戳破的呼吸球
撞上喷嘴，那就让气泡一跃而泄。
我的喉口一套上蠕虫样的绳索，就去威吓
带补丁场景处害病的爱。

"所有的游戏规则适用你的一轮斗鸡：
我将蒙上灯彻底搜寻罗网般的树林，
啄食，奔跑，在喷泉上舞蹈，躲闪时光，
在我急蹲之前，阴魂手持锤子、空气
击打光芒，血染喧闹的房室。

"如果我皱皮猴样的降生太残忍，
那就愤然将我塞回创生的房室。我松开手
随你缝补深邃的房门。这产床是个交叉地。
如果我的旅行带来痛楚，那就把方向弯成弧形
或者变成自由柔软的形态，跃过九个消瘦的月份。"

"不。即便是基督耀眼的产床
或者酣睡在迷人柔软的梦境，亲爱的，
我也不愿交换我的泪水或你坚硬的头骨。
我的女儿或儿子，刺穿我，逃离我，真的没关系，
哪怕整个沉闷天国的水域都破裂。

狄兰·托马斯诗选

207

Dylan Thomas

---

① 1939年4月首次发表于《诗歌》（伦敦），庆贺诗人的大儿子出生而作。

'Now to awake husked of gestures and my joy like a cave
To the anguish and carrion, to the infant forever unfree,
O my lost love bounced from a good home;
The grain that hurries this way from the rim of the grave
Has a voice and a house, and there and here you must couch and cry.

'Rest beyond choice in the dust-appointed grain,
At the breast stored with seas. No return
Through the waves of the fat streets nor the skeleton's thin ways.
The grave and my calm body are shut to your coming as stone,
And the endless beginning of prodigies suffers open.'

"此刻唤醒去荚的身姿，我的快乐仿佛一处洞穴
释放痛苦和腐肉，释放从不自由的婴儿，
哦，我失去的爱在温暖的家园跳跃；
谷粒从坟墓的边缘匆匆赶来
有了房子和声音，你可以不时地打滚与哭闹。

"别无选择，安息在尘埃相约的颗粒，
安息在胸怀大海的乳房。别回来，
穿越波涌的肉街或穿越身骨的瘦路。
坟墓和我宁静的躯体，仿佛石块拒绝你的光临，
神童那无限的源头经受着开放。"

Twenty-four years

Twenty-four years remind the tears of my eyes.
(Bury the dead for fear that they walk to the grave in labour.)
In the groin of the natural doorway I crouched like a tailor
Sewing a shroud for a journey
By the light of the meat-eating sun.
Dressed to die, the sensual strut begun,
With my red veins full of money,
In the final direction of the elementary town
I advance for as long as forever is.

二十四年[①]

二十四年唤起我眼中的泪水。
（掩埋死者，唯恐她们在分娩中走向坟墓。）
在腹股沟的自然门口，我像裁缝一样蜷缩
在食肉的光亮下
缝制一件上路的寿衣。
着衣而亡，肉欲开始阔步而行，
我红色的血管灌满金钱，
朝着小镇最后的方向
我昂首前行，直至永远。

① 1938 年 12 月首次发表于《今日生活与书信》。

The conversation of prayers

The conversation of prayers about to be said
By the child going to bed and the man on the stairs
Who climbs to his dying love in her high room,
The one not caring to whom in his sleep he will move
And the other full of tears that she will be dead,

Turns in the dark on the sound they know will arise
Into the answering skies from the green ground,
From the man on the stairs and the child by his bed.
The sound about to be said in the two prayers
For the sleep in a safe land and the love who dies

Will be the same grief flying. Whom shall they calm?
Shall the child sleep unharmed or the man be crying?
The conversation of prayers about to be said
Turns on the quick and the dead, and the man on the stairs
Tonight shall find no dying but alive and warm

In the fire of his care his love in the high room.
And the child not caring to whom he climbs his prayer
Shall drown in a grief as deep as his true grave,
And mark the dark eyed wave, through the eyes of sleep,
Dragging him up the stairs to one who lies dead.

祈祷者的对话①

祈祷者的对话即将要上演，
上床就寝的男孩和上楼的男子
爬向楼上房内垂死的爱人，
一个不在乎睡梦中他会走向谁，
另一个噙满眼泪，她行将死去，

黑暗里开启的祈祷声将会升起，
从绿色大地升入回应的天空，
从楼梯口的男子和床前的孩子。
两位祈祷者即将发出的声音，
为了平安入梦乡和垂死的爱人，

一样的伤悲在飞翔。他们抚慰谁？
孩子安然入梦乡还是男子在哭泣？
祈祷者的对话即将上演
开启生者与死者，而楼梯口的男子
今夜不见死亡，只见温情和生机

激发火一样热情照看楼上的爱人。
孩子不在乎爬向谁，他的祈祷将
溺死在真墓穴般深不可测的伤悲，
透过睡梦的双眸，留意黑眼的波涛
正将他拖往楼上奄奄一息的爱人。

① 写于 1945 年 3 月，1945 年 7 月首次发表于《今日生活与书信》。

Poem in October

It was my thirtieth year to heaven
Woke to my hearing from harbour and neighbour wood
And the mussel pooled and the heron
Priested shore
The morning beckon
With water praying and call of seagull and rook
And the knock of sailing boats on the net webbed wall
Myself to set foot
That second
In the still sleeping town and set forth.

My birthday began with the water-
Birds and the birds of the winged trees flying my name
Above the farms and the white horses
And I rose
In rainy autumn
And walked abroad in a shower of all my days.
High tide and the heron dived when I took the road
Over the border
And the gates
Of the town closed as the town awoke.

A springful of larks in a rolling

十月献诗①

这是我迈向天国的第三十个春秋
醒来听到一丝声响传自港湾及毗邻的森林
  传自贝壳聚集以及苍鹭布道的
    堤岸
    黎明召唤着
祈祷的海水、鸣叫的海鸥和白嘴鸦
千舸帆影一声声拍打渔网密布的岸墙
    催促我启程
    那一刻
  小镇依然沉睡，而我却已起身。

  我的生日始于这一片水鸟
那林中翻飞的鸟群翻飞我的名字
  越过农庄以及白色的马群
    我起身
    在此多雨的秋天
走出户外，过往的岁月纷至沓来。
潮水高涨，苍鹭扎入水中，此刻我取道
    越过边境
    而城门
  依然紧闭，尽管小镇已醒来。

  泉水般的云雀在翻卷的云海里

① 写于 1944 年 8 月，1945 年 2 月首次发表于《地平线》。

狄兰·托马斯诗选

Dylan Thomas

215

Cloud and the roadside bushes brimming with whistling
    Blackbirds and the sun of October
        Summery
      On the hill's shoulder,
Here were fond climates and sweet singers suddenly
Come in the morning where I wandered and listened
     To the rain wringing
       Wind blow cold
  In the wood faraway under me.

    Pale rain over the dwindling harbour
And over the sea wet church the size of a snail
    With its horns through mist and the castle
       Brown as owls
     But all the gardens
Of spring and summer were blooming in the tall tales
Beyond the border and under the lark full cloud.
     There could I marvel
      My birthday
  Away but the weather turned around.

    It turned away from the blithe country
And down the other air and the blue altered sky
    Streamed again a wonder of summer
      With apples
     Pears and red currants
And I saw in the turning so clearly a child's
Forgotten mornings when he walked with his mother
    Through the parables

翱翔，道旁的灌木丛栖满一群啁啾的黑鸟

　　十月夏天似的阳光

　　　　　照耀着

　　　　这片崇山峻岭，

这儿气候宜人，甜美的歌声猛然间

飘入清晨，我独自漫游其间，倾听

　　　　雨水吱吱地落下

　　　　　寒风

从我身下刮向远处的树林。

　　　　苍茫的雨落在小小的港湾

淋湿了海边那座蜗牛般大小的教堂

　　　它的触角穿越云雾和城堡

　　　　　猫头鹰般棕黄

　　　　而春夏所有的花园

难以置信地一起在故事中绽放花朵

远在边境之外，雾海云雀之下。

　　　　我在此感叹

　　　　　生日的

　　神奇，而气候却开始转换。

　　　　离开那一片欢乐的国度

随另一片气流而下，变幻的蓝色天空

　　　再次流淌一个夏天的神奇

　　　　　结满苹果、

　　　　香梨和红醋栗

在此转换中，我是如此清晰地看清

一个孩子遗忘的早晨，他和母亲一道

　　　　走过阳光下的

Of sun light

And the legends of the green chapels

And the twice told fields of infancy

That his tears burned my cheeks and his heart moved in mine.

These were the woods the river and sea

Where a boy

In the listening

Summertime of the dead whispered the truth of his joy

To the trees and the stones and the fish in the tide.

And the mystery

Sang alive

Still in the water and singingbirds.

And there could I marvel my birthday

Away but the weather turned around. And the true

Joy of the long dead child sang burning

In the sun.

It was my thirtieth

Year to heaven stood there then in the summer noon

Though the town below lay leaved with October blood.

O may my heart's truth

Still be sung

On this high hill in a year's turning.

寓言

走过绿色礼拜堂的传奇

　　　而再次聊起孩提时的田野
他的泪水灼热我的脸庞，他的心随我的心房跳动。
　　这些就是森林、河流和大海
　　　　　一个男孩
　　　在逝者聆听的夏日里
向树林、向石块，向潮水里的鱼儿
低声倾诉他内心欢乐的真情。
　　　　　而那份神秘依然
　　　　　生动地
在水中，在鸣叫的鸟群里歌唱。

　　　而我在此感叹生日的神奇
气候却早已开始转换。男孩长眠已久
　　他欢乐的真情在歌唱，在阳光下
　　　　燃烧。
　　　这是我迈向天国的
第三十个春秋，伫立于此，夏日的正午
山下小镇上的片片叶子，沾染十月的血色。
　　　哦，愿我心中的真情
　　　　依然被吟唱
　　在这高高的山巅，在这交替的岁月。

To Others than You

Friend by enemy I call you out.

You with a bad coin in your socket,
You my friend there with a winning air
Who palmed the lie on me when you looked
Brassily at my shyest secret,
Enticed with twinkling bits of the eye
Till the sweet tooth of my love bit dry,
Rasped at last, and I stumbled and sucked,
Whom now I conjure to stand as thief
In the memory worked by mirrors,
With unforgettably smiling act,
Quickness of hand in the velvet glove
And my whole heart under your hammer,
Were once such a creature, so gay and frank
A desireless familiar
I never thought to utter or think
While you displaced a truth in the air,

That though I loved them for their faults
As much as for their good,
My friends were enemies on stilts
With their heads in a cunning cloud.

致你及他人①

密友啊仇敌，我叫你出来。

你的眼里窝着一枚臭硬币，
朋友，你一副洋洋得意的神态，
贪心地窥视我最羞涩的秘密，
掌心里塞给我一把谎言，
诱惑的眼神贼亮贼亮，
直到我甜蜜的爱牙不再湿润，
最终咬得咯咯响，我踉跄，我抽泣，
此刻我咒你贼一样现身
在镜子映照的记忆里，
一脸难忘的笑容，
手戴丝绒手套身姿矫健，
我整个身心遭受你的锤击，
生命一度那么快乐、那么坦诚，
无欲无求，亲密无间，
我也从未想过表述或思索
而你却错置了一种真情在空中；

尽管他们的美好和过错我一样地爱，
我的爱依然如故，
朋友们却成了踩着高跷的敌人，
他们的脑壳翘到狡诈的云层里。

---

① 写于 1939 年 5 月，1939 年秋首次发表于《七》。

Love in the Asylum

A stranger has come
To share my room in the house not right in the head,
A girl mad as birds

Bolting the night of the door with her arm her plume.
Strait in the mazed bed
She deludes the heaven-proof house with entering clouds

Yet she deludes with walking the nightmarish room,
At large as the dead,
Or rides the imagined oceans of the male wards.

She has come possessed
Who admits the delusive light through the bouncing wall,
Possessed by the skies

She sleeps in the narrow trough yet she walks the dust
Yet raves at her will
On the madhouse boards worn thin by my walking tears.

And taken by light in her arms at long and dear last
I may without fail
Suffer the first vision that set fire to the stars.

疯人院里的爱①

有一位陌生人
要来和我同住，脑子有点不正常，
有一位女孩疯如鸟

她用臂膀和翅翼，闩住门内的黑夜。
束缚于迷惘的病床，
她让涌入的流云迷惑不见天堂的房舍，

她还漫游于噩梦似的房间，迷离恍惚，
死尸般逍遥自在
或者骑马奔腾在男病房想象的海洋。

她来时已发疯
任凭迷惑的光线，穿透反弹的墙壁，
着魔于整个天空

她睡在狭小的料槽，还漫游于尘埃
仍然胡言乱语
我流淌的泪水，侵蚀疯人院的床板。

久久地或最终被她怀中的灵光所虏，
我也许一定得
忍受最初的幻影去点燃万千的星云。

---

① 1941 年 5—6 月首次发表于《诗歌》(伦敦)。

Unluckily for a death

Unluckily for a death
Waiting with phoenix under
The pyre yet to be lighted of my sins and days,
And for the woman in shades
Saint carved and sensual among the scudding
Dead and gone, dedicate forever to my self
Though the brawl of the kiss has not occurred,
On the clay cold mouth, on the fire
Branded forehead, that could bind
Her constant, nor the winds of love broken wide
To the wind the choir and cloister
Of the wintry nunnery of the order of lust
Beneath my life, that sighs for the seducer's coming
In the sun strokes of summer,

Loving on this sea banged guilt
My holy lucky body
Under the cloud against love is caught and held and kissed
In the mill of the midst
Of the descending day, the dark our folly,
Cut to the still star in the order of the quick
But blessed by such heroic hosts in your every
Inch and glance that the wound

不幸地等待死亡①

不幸地等待死亡
偕同凤凰一起等待
火葬的柴火即将点燃我罪孽的时光，
等待阴影里的女人
石刻的圣徒充满肉欲，夹杂着死者
风起云涌，向我的自我不断地奉献，
在肉身冰冷的嘴角，在烈火
烧烧的前额，那令她坚贞不渝
勃发的亲吻尽管还未响起，
爱的风暴也未随我的生命烟消云散，
在肉欲分明的冷漠女修道院，
风在回廊飘荡着唱诗班的歌声，
而渴望诱惑者到来的一声声叹息
随夏天阵阵热浪袭来，

在这罪恶肆虐的海面相爱，
我幸运的圣体
在爱的云层映衬下紧紧地相拥热烈地亲吻
随时光不断地碾磨，
我们愚蠢的黑暗
随生的节律被切成肃穆的星星，
而英勇的主人在你每一时每一瞥下
赐福于我，伤口必然

狄兰·托马斯诗选

Dylan Thomas

225

Is certain god, and the ceremony of souls
Is celebrated there, and communion between suns.
Never shall my self chant
About the saint in shades while the endless breviary
Turns of your prayed flesh, nor shall I shoo the bird below me:
The death biding two lie lonely.

I see the tigron in tears
In the androgynous dark,
His striped and noon maned tribe striding to holocaust,
The she mules bear their minotaurs,
The duck-billed platypus broody in a milk of birds.
I see the wanting nun saint carved in a garb
Of shades, symbol of desire beyond my hours
And guilts, great crotch and giant
Continence. I see the unfired phoenix, herald
And heaven crier, arrow now of aspiring
And the renouncing of islands.
All love but for the full assemblage in flower
Of the living flesh is monstrous or immortal,
And the grave its daughters.

Love, my fate got luckily,
Teaches with no telling
That the phoenix' bid for heaven and the desire after
Death in the carved nunnery
Both shall fail if I bow not to your blessing
Nor walk in the cool of your mortal garden
With immortality at my side like Christ the sky.

化为神，庆贺灵魂的诞生，
在阳光的相映下共享圣餐。
我的自我将永不颂唱
阴影下的圣徒，而无穷无尽的祈祷词
替换你祈祷的肉身，我也不嘘嘘地驱赶脚下的飞鸟：
死亡等待双方孤独地躺下。

我看见狮虎在流泪，
在阴阳交叉的黑暗里，
身纹斑斓、鬃毛浓密的兽群大步迈向毁灭，
母骡生养人身牛头怪，
鸭嘴兽在鸟的哺育下繁衍生息。
我看见渴望的圣女刻在阴影里，
欲望的象征超越我的时光与罪孽，
健硕的裤裆克制巨大的欲望。
我也看见未曾赴汤蹈火的凤凰，信使
和天堂的传呼员，此刻的渴望之箭
以及荒岛的与世隔绝。
除非活生生的肉体花团锦簇般开放
一切爱都将变得畸形或不朽，
坟墓化为它的女儿。

爱，我命里侥幸所获的爱
无言地启示
寻求天堂的凤凰和石刻女修道院里
死后的欲望都将烟消云散
如果我不鞠躬致谢你的祝福，
也不漫步在你凉爽的人间花园，
伴我身旁的永恒，仿佛基督伴随天国。

This I know from the native

Tongue of your translating eyes. The young stars told me,

Hurling into beginning like Christ the child.

Lucklessly she must lie patient

And the vaulting bird be still. O my true love, hold me.

In your every inch and glance is the globe of genesis spun,

And the living earth your sons.

我从你眼神传译的母语中
明白这一切。新生的星星告诉我，
快步投入初始，犹如基督投胎。
不幸的她须耐心地躺着，
屋顶上的鸟儿也须安静。哦，我的挚爱，拥抱我。
在你每一时每一瞥下，创世的天体开始转动，
这生机盎然的地球就是你的子孙。

Into her lying down head

I

Into her lying down head
His enemies entered bed,
Under the encumbered eyelid,
Through the rippled drum of the hair-buried ear;
And Noah's rekindled now unkind dove
Flew man-bearing there.
Last night in a raping wave
Whales unrefined from the green grave
In fountains of origin gave up their love,
Along her innocence glided
Juan aflame and savagely young King Lear,
Queen Catherine howling bare
And Samson drowned in his hair,
The colossal intimacies of silent
Once seen strangers or shades on a stair;
There the dark blade and wanton sighing her down
To a haycock couch and the scythes of his arms

① 1940 年 11 月首次发表于《今日生活与书信》。
② 诺亚（Noah），《圣经》人物，据说诺亚是拉麦的儿子，活了 950 岁。在罪孽深重的人群中，只有诺亚在上帝眼前蒙恩，上帝选中了诺亚一家，建造方舟避过大洪水。
③ 唐璜（Don Juan），诗人拜伦的一部长篇诗体小说《唐璜》里的人物，生性风流，喜与姑娘们胡搅蛮缠，不受道德规范的任何约束。
④ 李尔王（King Lear），莎士比亚名剧《李尔王》中的悲剧人物。李尔王不察善恶而导致无处安身，浪迹荒野，最后在精神与肉体的折磨中，在

进入她躺下的头颅①

1

进入她躺下的头颅，

　　他的情敌来到床头

在略显沉重的眼皮底下，

穿越头发遮掩下发出潺潺震颤声的耳膜；

此刻诺亚②被重新点燃，无情的鸽子

　　　　飞离孕育人类的营地。

　　昨晚在猛烈的浪涛中，

　　鲸鱼未经绿色坟墓的锤炼，

在源初的喷泉口放弃他们的爱，

　　随着她的纯真滑过

燃情的唐璜③，残暴的青年李尔王④，

　　　　赤裸哀嚎的凯瑟琳皇后⑤

　　　　与淹没于头发的参孙⑥，

寂静中的极度亲昵一度见之于

　　楼梯口的陌生人及其阴影；

那黑色的刀锋和荡妇叹息她

在干草床躺下，在拂晓啼鸣之前，

失去所爱而无法承受的悲哀中结束人生。

⑤ 凯瑟琳皇后（Queen Catherine），在俄国历史上与彼得大帝齐名，建立了人类历史上空前绝后的庞大帝国，但后人最关注的还是她那一段段令人目不暇接的情史。

⑥ 参孙（Samson），《圣经》人物。据说出生时天使告诉他母亲，他的力量将会来自他的头发。参孙却放纵肉欲，挡不住女色的诱惑，泄露了超人力气的秘密，后因头发被剪，力量全失，受尽羞辱。

Rode and whistled a hundred times

Before the crowing morning climbed;

Man was the burning England she was sleep-walking, and the

enamouring island

Made her limbs blind by luminous charms,

Sleep to a newborn sleep in a swaddling loin-leaf stroked and sang

And his runaway beloved childlike laid in the acorned sand.

II

There where a numberless tongue

Wound their room with a male moan,

His faith around her flew undone

And darkness hung the walls with baskets of snakes,

A furnace-nostrilled column-membered

Super-or-near man

Resembling to her dulled sense

The thief of adolescence,

Early imaginary half remembered

Oceanic lover alone

Jealousy cannot forget for all her sakes,

Made his bad bed in her good

Night, and enjoyed as he would.

Crying, white gowned, from the middle moonlit stages

Out to the tiered and hearing tide,

Close and far she announced the theft of the heart

In the taken body at many ages,

Trespasser and broken bride

Celebrating at her side

All blood-signed assailings and vanished marriages in which he

had no lovely part

他镰刀状的臂膀

　　一次次呼啸着前行；

男人是燃烧的英格兰，她梦游其中，

　　　迷人岛屿

　　夺目的魅力销魂她的肢体，

新生儿般腰间裹着叶片入眠，尽享抚摩和诵唱，

他逃离的爱人天真无邪地置身于落满橡子的沙丘。

2

　　　那数不清的口舌环绕

　　　　他们的房室发出男人的呜咽，

　　　他的忠诚围着她不息地飞翔，

而黑暗在一堵堵墙头挂起一篮篮毒蛇，

一位体魄魁梧、鼻息浓烈的男子，

　　　　几乎完美，

　　　　朦胧中她感奋他像极

　　　　青春期的贼子，

源初的想象依稀可见大洋般

　　　　孤独的情人

嫉妒更不能全因她而忘却，

　　　　　他铺开罪恶之床，

　　　　　在她美好之夜尽情享乐。

哭喊，身着白色的睡袍，从月明的舞台中央

　　走向轰鸣而层层推进的潮汐，

她时近时远地宣称这偷心的贼子

侵占她的身体已多年，

　　　　入侵者及其破损的新娘

　　　　在她一旁庆贺

一切血示的质询及消亡的婚姻，对此他未曾感奋

　　　　丝毫的美好

Nor could share, for his pride, to the least

Mutter and foul wingbeat of the solemnizing nightpriest

Her holy unholy hours with the always anonymous beast.

III

Two sand grains together in bed,

Head to heaven-circling head,

Singly lie with the whole wide shore,

The covering sea their nightfall with no names;

And out of every domed and soil-based shell

One voice in chains declaims

The female, deadly, and male

Libidinous betrayal,

Golden dissolving under the water veil.

A she bird sleeping brittle by

Her lover's wings that fold tomorrow's flight,

Within the nested treefork

Sings to the treading hawk

Carrion, paradise, chirrup my bright yolk.

A blade of grass longs with the meadow,

A stone lies lost and locked in the lark-high hill.

Open as to the air to the naked shadow

O she lies alone and still,

Innocent between two wars,

With the incestuous secret brother in the seconds to perpetuate

the stars,

A man torn up mourns in the sole night.

And the second comers, the severers, the enemies from the deep

Forgotten dark, rest their pulse and bury their dead in her

faithless sleep.

也不曾，因他的傲慢，至少分享
庄严的牧师夜间扑动污秽的翅翼发出的喃喃话语。
她神圣又非神圣的时刻与始终匿名的野兽同在。

3

两粒沙聚拢在床头，
头对头地环绕天堂，
孤单地躺在无比宽广的海岸，
大海覆盖他们无名的黄昏；
每一枚基于泥土的半球形贝壳传来
一阵阵声音宣告
这女人奄奄一息，而男人
好色背叛，
在水的遮掩下金黄般消融。
一只脆弱的雌鸟睡在一旁，
情人的翅翼收拢起明日的飞行，
在筑巢的树杈间
向交尾的鹰诵唱
腐尸，天堂，我明亮的卵黄喊喊地叫。
一叶草融入草坪才能长存，
一粒石禁闭在云雀的山岗会迷失自己。
向着裸露的阴影开放，仿佛向着天空，
哦，她躺着，孤独而宁静，
这两次战争间的无辜者，
而暗地乱伦的兄弟片刻间让星星
趋于不朽，
一位男子在孤独夜晚撕去哀痛。
第二批来访者，撕裂者情敌，来自深深遗忘的黑暗，
休眠自身的脉动，在她不忠的睡眠中
掩埋他们的死者。

Do not go gentle into that good night

Do not go gentle into that good night,
Old age should burn and rave at close of day;
Rage, rage against the dying of the light.

Though wise men at their end know dark is right,
Because their words had forked no lightning they
Do not go gentle into that good night.

Good men, the last wave by, crying how bright
Their frail deeds might have danced in a green bay,
Rage, rage against the dying of the light.

Wild men who caught and sang the sun in flight,
And learn, too late, they grieved it on its way,
Do not go gentle into that good night.

Grave men, near death, who see with blinding sight
Blind eyes could blaze like meteors and be gay,
Rage, rage against the dying of the light.

And you, my father, there on the sad height,
Curse, bless, me now with your fierce tears, I pray.
Do not go gentle into that good night.
Rage, rage against the dying of the light.

不要温顺地走进那个良宵[①]

不要温顺地走进那个良宵，
老年在日暮之时应当燃烧与咆哮；
怒斥，怒斥光明的消亡。

临终时明智的人虽然懂得黑暗逍遥，
因为他们的话语已迸不出丝毫电光，
却不要温顺地走进那个良宵。

善良的人翻腾最后一浪，高呼着辉煌，
他们脆弱的善行曾在绿色港湾里跳荡，
怒斥，怒斥光明的消亡。

狂暴的人曾抓住并诵唱飞翔的太阳，
虽然为时太晚，却明了途中的哀伤，
不要温顺地走进那个良宵。

肃穆的人，临近死亡，透过眩目的视野，
失明的双眸可以像流星一样欢欣闪耀，
怒斥，怒斥光明的消亡。

而您，我的父亲，在这悲哀之巅，
此刻我求您，用热泪诅咒我，祝福我。
不要温顺地走进那个良宵。
怒斥，怒斥光明的消亡。

① 1951 年 5 月为他父亲而作，1951 年 11 月首次发表于《博特奥斯克》。

狄兰·托马斯诗选

Dylan Thomas

237

Deaths and Entrances

On almost the incendiary eve
    Of several near deaths,
When one at the great least of your best loved
    And always known must leave
Lions and fires of his flying breath,
    Of your immortal friends
Who'd raise the organs of the counted dust
    To shoot and sing your praise,
One who called deepest down shall hold his peace
    That cannot sink or cease
    Endlessly to his wound
In many married London's estranging grief.

On almost the incendiary eve
    When at your lips and keys,
Locking, unlocking, the murdered strangers weave,
    One who is most unknown,
Your polestar neighbour, sun of another street,
    Will dive up to his tears.
He'll bathe his raining blood in the male sea
    Who strode for your own dead
And wind his globe out of your water thread
    And load the throats of shells

死亡与入口①

有些人在濒临死亡

　　即将燃烧的前夕,

至少你最挚爱的一个人

　　　总算明白必须告别

名流和烈火般飞扬的气息,

　　在你不朽的朋友中

有人会提高嗓门,尽管被视作尘土

　　勃发地诵唱对你的赞美,

一个最深沉的人会闭口缄默

　　　永不沉没或终结

　　　他的伤痛

那众多伦敦已婚夫妇疏远的伤悲。

在即将燃烧的前夕,

　　你的双唇和钥匙,

紧锁或开启,被害的陌生人迂回行进,

　　一个最不了解的人

你北极星上的邻居,另一街区的太阳,

　　会潜入到他的泪水。

他将在雄性的海洋濯洗他雨水般的血液

　　因你的死亡而大步疾走,

他让你的水线缠绕他的世界

　　让空壳的喉口塞满

---

① 1941 年 1 月首次发表于《地平线》。

With every cry since light
Flashed first across his thunderclapping eyes.

On almost the incendiary eve
    Of deaths and entrances,
When near and strange wounded on London's waves
    Have sought your single grave,
One enemy, of many, who knows well
    Your heart is luminous
In the watched dark, quivering through locks and caves,
    Will pull the thunderbolts
To shut the sun, plunge, mount your darkened keys
    And sear just riders back,
    Until that one loved least
Looms the last Samson of your zodiac.

每一声哭喊，自从
第一丝光亮闪过他霹雳雾般的眼睛。

在死亡与入口
　　即将燃烧的前夕，
亲近的和陌生的受伤于伦敦的波涛，
　　寻找你孤独的坟墓，
众敌之一，熟知
　　你那颗明亮之心
照亮黑暗时，颤动着穿越锁孔和洞穴，
　　终将扯起雷霆
遮蔽太阳，插入，开启你幽暗的钥匙，
　　热浪仅逼迫骑手后退，
　　直到至少还爱你的人
逼近你黄道带上最后的参孙。

On a Wedding Anniversary

The sky is torn across
This ragged anniversary of two
Who moved for three years in tune
Down the long walks of their vows.

Now their love lies a loss
And Love and his patients roar on a chain;
From every true or crater
Carrying cloud, Death strikes their house.

Too late in the wrong rain
They come together whom their love parted:
The windows pour into their heart
And the doors burn in their brain.

结婚周年纪念日①

天空被撕破
穿过俩人这褴褛的纪念日，
三年来他们和睦相处
携手走过誓约长长的小道。

此刻爱已丧失
爱神和他的病人在同一锁链下哀嚎；
从每个真理或火山口
死神挟来阴云，敲击他们的房门。

错误的雨中，一切太晚
他们相聚相会，爱却已分离：
窗户倾入他们的心扉
房门在大脑里燃烧。

① 1941 年 1 月 15 日首次发表于《诗歌》（伦敦），五年后经修订收入诗集
《死亡与入口》。

狄兰·托马斯诗选

Dylan Thomas

243

On the Marriage of a Virgin

Waking alone in a multitude of loves when morning's light
Surprised in the opening of her nightlong eyes
His golden yesterday asleep upon the iris
And this day's sun leapt up the sky out of her thighs
Was miraculous virginity old as loaves and fishes,
Though the moment of a miracle is unending lightning
And the shipyards of Galilee's footprints hide a navy of doves.

No longer will the vibrations of the sun desire on
Her deepsea pillow where once she married alone,
Her heart all ears and eyes, lips catching the avalanche
Of the golden ghost who ringed with his streams her mercury bone,
Who under the lids of her windows hoisted his golden luggage,
For a man sleeps where fire leapt down and she learns through his arm
That other sun, the jealous coursing of the unrivalled blood.

处女新婚①

在情意绵绵的夜晚独自醒来，晨光
惊愕于她彻夜未眠的眼睛
他金色的昨日在虹膜上沉睡
今日的太阳从她的大腿跃上天空
无比神奇纯洁而古老，仿佛面包和游鱼，
虽然圣迹的瞬间只是无休止的闪电
留存足迹的加利利②船坞掩藏一大群鸽子。

太阳的震颤不再渴望她深海般的枕头
她在那里一度独自成婚，她的心，
她的耳朵，她的眼睛，她的双唇俘获他雪崩般
金色的灵魂，她水银般的身骨响彻他潺潺的溪流，
他从她那眼睑般的窗口扯起他金色的行李，
一团火焰跃过他的沉睡之地，她从他的怀抱中
懂得另一轮太阳，无敌的血液小心地奔流。

① 1941 年 10 月首次发表于《今日生活与书信》，最早的版本可见于 1933
　　年 3 月的笔记本。
② 加利利（Galilee），巴勒斯坦北部一多山地区，据说耶稣童年的家就在
　　加利利的拿撒勒，并留有圣迹。

狄兰·托马斯诗选

245

Dylan Thomas

In my craft or sullen art

In my craft or sullen art
Exercised in the still night
When only the moon rages
And the lovers lie abed
With all their griefs in their arms,
I labour by singing light
Not for ambition or bread
Or the strut and trade of charms
On the ivory stages
But for the common wages
Of their most secret heart.

Not for the proud man apart
From the raging moon I write
On these spindrift pages
Nor for the towering dead
With their nightingales and psalms
But for the lovers, their arms
Round the griefs of the ages,
Who pay no praise or wages
Nor heed my craft or art.

我的手艺或沉寂的诗艺①

我的手艺或沉寂的诗艺
操演在宁静的夜晚
此时唯有月亮在发怒
恋人们躺在床上
满怀他们一身的忧伤，
我在灯光的吟唱下写作
不是为野心或面包
也不是为炫耀
或在象牙舞台上卖弄风骚
而是为他们内心最深处
极普通的回报。

除了愤怒的月亮
我不为自傲的人
铺开浪花四溅的纸笺
也不为高耸的死尸
伴随夜莺和诗篇而写作
而是为了恋人们
他们怀抱岁月的忧伤，
不赐予赞美或酬劳
也不留意我的手艺或诗艺。

狄兰·托马斯诗选

Dylan Thomas

---

① 1945 年 10 月首次发表于《今日生活与书信》。

Lie still, sleep becalmed

Lie still, sleep becalmed, sufferer with the wound
In the throat, burning and turning. All night afloat
On the silent sea we have heard the sound
That came from the wound wrapped in the salt sheet.

Under the mile off moon we trembled listening
To the sea sound flowing like blood from the loud wound
And when the salt sheet broke in a storm of singing
The voices of all the drowned swam on the wind.

Open a pathway through the slow sad sail,
Throw wide to the wind the gates of the wandering boat
For my voyage to begin to the end of my wound,
We heard the sea sound sing, we saw the salt sheet tell.
Lie still, sleep becalmed, hide the mouth in the throat,
Or we shall obey, and ride with you through the drowned.

静静地躺下，安然入睡①

静静地躺下，安然入睡，患者
喉咙里的伤口，火烧火燎。我们
整夜漂浮在寂静的大海，听到
一丝声响传自咸床单包扎的伤口。

我们站在数里外的月光下瑟瑟发抖，
倾听大海奔流，仿佛鲜血流自喧闹的伤口，
而当咸床单在风暴般的歌声里崩裂，
所有溺水者的呼救在风中向前游动。

缓慢而忧伤的航行打开一条通道，
我们迎着狂风敞开漂泊小船的大门，
我的航行始于伤口归于伤口，
我们听到大海的歌声，看到咸床单的倾诉。
静静地躺下，安然入睡，嘴藏进喉咙，
或我们屈从，与你同行，穿越溺水的阴魂。

① 首次发表于 1945 年 6 月《今日生活与书信》。

Fern Hill

Now as I was young and easy under the apple boughs
About the lilting house and happy as the grass was green,
    The night above the dingle starry,
        Time let me hail and climb
    Golden in the heydays of his eyes,
And honoured among wagons I was prince of the apple towns
And once below a time I lordly had the trees and leaves
        Trail with daisies and barley
    Down the rivers of the windfall light.

And as I was green and carefree, famous among the barns
About the happy yard and singing as the farm was home,
    In the sun that is young once only,
        Time let me play and be
    Golden in the mercy of his means,
And green and golden I was huntsman and herdsman, the calves
Sang to my horn, the foxes on the hills barked clear and cold,
        And the sabbath rang slowly
    In the pebbles of the holy streams.

All the sun long it was running, it was lovely, the hay
Fields high as the house, the tunes from the chimneys, it was air
        And playing, lovely and watery

羊齿山①

此刻我站在苹果树下，年轻又飘逸，
身旁的小屋活泼轻快，我幸福美好，绿草如茵，
　　幽谷上的夜空星光灿烂，
　　　　　时光令我欢呼雀跃
　　　　眼中的盛世金碧辉煌，
我是苹果小镇的王子，马车迎送，无比的荣耀，
很久以后我像君王一样拥有森林和绿叶
　　　　沿途长满雏菊和大麦
　　　　河岸上微风吹拂洒落的阳光。

此刻我青春无忧，声名赫赫，四周谷仓座座，
幸福的庭院深深，我一路欢歌，仿佛农场就是家园
　　　　阳光也曾一度年轻，
　　　　　　时光让我嬉戏，
　　　　　蒙受他的恩宠金光闪耀
我是猎手，我是牧人，年轻灿烂，牛犊们应着
我的号角歌唱，山岗上狐狸吠声清脆而苍凉，
　　　　　圣溪的鹅卵石里
　　　　传来安息日缓缓的钟声。

明媚的阳光整天地泼洒，那么美丽可爱，
田间的干草高及屋脊，烟囱飘出美妙的旋律，
　　　那是嬉戏的空气，动人又湿润，

And fire green as grass.
　　And nightly under the simple stars
As I rode to sleep the owls were bearing the farm away,
All the moon long I heard, blessed among stables, the nightjars
　　Flying with the ricks, and the horses
　　　　Flashing into the dark.

And then to awake, and the farm, like a wanderer white
With the dew, come back, the cock on his shoulder: it was all
　　Shining, it was Adam and maiden,
　　　　The sky gathered again
　　And the sun grew round that very day.
So it must have been after the birth of the simple light
In the first, spinning place, the spellbound horses walking warm
　　Out of the whinnying green stable
　　　　On to the fields of praise.

And honoured among foxes and pheasants by the gay house
Under the new made clouds and happy as the heart was long,
　　In the sun born over and over,
　　　　I ran my heedless ways,
　　My wishes raced through the house high hay
And nothing I cared, at my sky blue trades, that time allows
In all his tuneful turning so few and such morning songs
　　Before the children green and golden
　　　　Follow him out of grace,

Nothing I cared, in the lamb white days, that time would take me
Up to the swallow thronged loft by the shadow of my hand,

　　　　　　　而火焰青翠如绿草。

　　　　每到夜色降临，稀疏的星空下
我赶着回家入睡，猫头鹰驮着农场而去，
皎洁的月光整夜地赐福，我在马厩听到欧夜鹰
　　　　衔起干草飞翔，一匹匹马
　　　　　　　光一样闪入黑夜。

随后农场醒来，像一位流浪者身披白露
再次回归，肩上立着雄鸡：阳光普照大地
　　　　那是亚当和夏娃，
　　　　　　　天空再次聚拢
　　　　那一天的太阳浑圆无边。
所以肯定是质朴的光芒诞生之后
在最初旋转的地方，痴迷的马群温情地
　　　　走出低声嘶鸣的绿色马厩
　　　　　　　奔驰在美好的原野。

快乐的小屋旁，我荣幸地置身于狐群和雉鸡旁
新近形成的云朵下，幸福欢畅，内心悠长，
　　　　太阳日复一日地诞生，
　　　　　　我狂放不羁，
　　　　我的祝愿穿越高及屋脊的干草，
在蓝天下劳作，无忧无虑，时光在和谐的
旋律里转动，竟诵唱如此寥寥几首晨歌，
　　　　随后散发青春活力的孩子
　　　　　　随他步出优雅，

我无所牵挂，在羔羊般洁白的日子里，时光
拉起我手的影子，在冉冉升起的月光下，

In the moon that is always rising,
    Nor that riding to sleep
I should hear him fly with the high fields
And wake to the farm forever fled from the childless land.
Oh as I was young and easy in the mercy of his means,
    Time held me green and dying
    Though I sang in my chains like the sea.

爬上栖满燕子的阁楼，

　　　我并不一路奔波入眠，

　　我该听到他与高高的原野一起飞翔，

　醒来发现农场永远逃离了没有孩子的土地。

哦，我蒙受他的恩宠，年轻又飘逸，

　　　　时光赐我青春与死亡

　　尽管我戴着镣铐依然像大海一样歌唱。

In Country Sleep

Never and never, my girl riding far and near
In the land of the hearthstone tales, and spelled asleep,
Fear or believe that the wolf in a sheepwhite hood
Loping and bleating roughly and blithely shall leap,
                  My dear, my dear,
Out of a lair in the flocked leaves in the dew dipped year
To eat your heart in the house in the rosy wood.

Sleep, good, for ever, slow and deep, spelled rare and wise,
My girl ranging the night in the rose and shire
Of the hobnail tales: no gooseherd or swine will turn
Into a homestall king or hamlet of fire
                  And prince of ice
To court the honeyed heart from your side before sunrise
In a spinney of ringed boys and ganders, spike and burn,

Nor the innocent lie in the rooting dingle wooed
And staved, and riven among plumes my rider weep.
From the broomed witch's spume you are shielded by fern
And flower of country sleep and the greenwood keep.
                  Lie fast and soothed,
Safe be and smooth from the bellows of the rushy brood.

梦中的乡村①

1

我那远近一路驰骋的女孩
流连于梦中拼读炉边童话的原野，
别害怕或别相信，裹着羊毛头巾的狼
跳着脚奔跑，粗哑地发出咩咩的叫声，
　　　　　　　　我的宝贝，我的心肝，
在露珠浸润的日子，欢快地跳出落叶满地的狼窝
窜入玫瑰林的房子吞食你的心肝。

睡吧，慢慢地酣然入睡，不要过于沉迷拼读，
我的女孩在夜晚漫游乡村童话里的玫瑰和州郡：
牧鹅人或猪绝不会变成农家院落里的国王
或火一般热烈的哈姆雷特
　　　　　　　　冰一样冷酷的王子，
蜂拥在灌木林的男孩和雄鹅，发狂而叮当作响
拂晓前，设法从你那儿获取那颗蜜糖般的心，

天真的谎言也不会在生根的幽谷求欢
与打孔，并在我骑手哭泣的羽毛间撕裂。
羊齿草一再替你挡开女巫扫泼的泡沫，
乡村的花朵入睡，翠绿的树林默然看护。
　　　　　　　　快快地躺下睡吧，
安然又宁静，滑离灯心草丛呼呼的风声。

① 1947 年 12 月首次发表于《地平线》。

Never, my girl, until tolled to sleep by the stern

Bell believe or fear that the rustic shade or spell
Shall harrow and snow the blood while you ride wide and near,
For who unmanningly haunts the mountain ravened eaves
Or skulks in the dell moon but moonshine echoing clear
                              From the starred well?
A hill touches an angel! Out of a saint's cell
The nightbird lauds through nunneries and domes of leaves

Her robin breasted tree, three Marys in the rays.
Sanctum sanctorum the animal eye of the wood
In the rain telling its beads, and the gravest ghost
The owl at its knelling. Fox and holt kneel before blood.
                              Now the tales praise
The star rise at pasture and nightlong the fables graze
On the lord's-table of the bowing grass. Fear most

For ever of all not the wolf in his baaing hood
Nor the tusked prince, in the ruttish farm, at the rind
And mire of love, but the Thief as meek as the dew.
The country is holy: O bide in that country kind,
                              Know the green good,
Under the prayer wheeling moon in the rosy wood
Be shielded by chant and flower and gay may you

Lie in grace. Sleep spelled at rest in the lowly house
In the squirrel nimble grove, under linen and thatch
And star: held and blessed, though you scour the high four

我的女孩，除非丧钟鸣响，摇你入梦乡

钟声从不相信或害怕野外的影子或符咒
在你远近一路驰骋时，会耙犁或雪埋你的鲜血，
谁会幽灵般怯懦地出没寒鸦栖息的山崖？
除了月光在群星璀璨的井口清越地回响
            谁会隐匿于月明的幽谷？
山岗触及天使！夜莺赞美的歌声飘自
圣人的小屋，穿越女修道院和落叶斑斓的屋顶，

知更鸟落在树梢，三圣母玛利亚在月光下闪现。
至高无上的至圣所，林中动物的眼睛
在雨中水珠般倾诉，最阴森的幽灵猫头鹰
发出不祥的哀鸣。狐狸和林地跪在血泊里。
            此刻童话颂扬
星星在草场上空升起，彻夜地放牧寓言
在绿草摇曳的圣桌。永远不必害怕

裹着羊毛头巾咩咩叫的狼，也不必害怕
长着獠牙的王子，在春情荡漾的农庄陷入
爱情的泥潭，但是要警惕那露水般温顺的贼。
乡村多么神圣：哦，住在自然亲切的乡村里，
            感奋绿野的美好，
玫瑰林中的月光在祈祷者的脚下飘荡，
愿歌声和鲜花庇护你，愿你快乐永远

欣然就寝。安然入睡在松鼠窜动的小树林，
低矮的小屋，亚麻、茅草、星光遮蔽着屋顶：
愿你尽享神的祝福，虽然你穿越的狂风

Winds, from the dousing shade and the roarer at the latch,
Cool in your vows.
Yet out of the beaked, web dark and the pouncing boughs
Be you sure the Thief will seek a way sly and sure

And sly as snow and meek as dew blown to the thorn,
This night and each vast night until the stern bell talks
In the tower and tolls to sleep over the stalls
Of the hearthstone tales my own, last love; and the soul walks
The waters shorn.
This night and each night since the falling star you were born,
Ever and ever he finds a way, as the snow falls,

As the rain falls, hail on the fleece, as the vale mist rides
Through the haygold stalls, as the dew falls on the wind-
Milled dust of the apple tree and the pounded islands
Of the morning leaves, as the star falls, as the winged
Apple seed glides,
And falls, and flowers in the yawning wound at our sides,
As the world falls, silent as the cyclone of silence.

II

Night and the reindeer on the clouds above the haycocks
And the wings of the great roc ribboned for the fair!
The leaping saga of prayer! And high, there, on the hare
Heeled winds the rooks
Cawing from their black bethels soaring, the holy books
Of birds! Among the cocks like fire the red fox

刮自四处潮湿的影子和咆哮的锁孔，

　　　　　　　　尽管誓言那么冷漠。
但是走出鸟嘴、蛛网的黑暗和摇动的树枝，
别忘记那贼正偷偷而执着地搜寻而来，

飞雪般隐秘，露珠般温顺地飘向荆棘，
就在今夜以及每一个辽阔的夜晚，直到丧钟
在塔楼里敲响，在炉边童话的马厩上空
送我自身最终的爱进入梦乡；灵魂走过

　　　　　　　　修剪一新的水面。
今夜以及你星星般降生后的每一个夜晚，
他不停地搜寻而来，犹如冬雪飘落，

雨点洒落，冰雹猛击羊群，犹如山谷里的迷雾
飘过干草般金黄的马厩，露珠飘落苹果树上
飞旋的尘土，飘落在晨叶击打的荒岛，
犹如星星陨落，犹如翻飞的苹果籽

　　　　　　　　轻轻地滑行
又飘落，鲜花般盛开在我们腰间开裂的伤口，
犹如世界沉落，犹如寂静的旋风无声无息。

　　　　　　　　　2
夜晚，驯鹿在干草堆上空的云层腾挪
大鹏为仙女装上展翅的双翼！
祈祷的英雄传奇遍布四方！在那兔子般

　　　　　　　　跃动的狂风里
白嘴鸦随高翔的黑色教堂啼鸣，一本飞鸟的圣书！
红色的狐狸在火一样的雄鸟间

Burning! Night and the vein of birds in the winged, sloe wrist

Of the wood! Pastoral beat of blood through the laced leaves!

The stream from the priest black wristed spinney and sleeves

Of thistling frost

Of the nightingale's din and tale! The upgiven ghost

Of the dingle torn to singing and the surpliced

Hill of cypresses! The din and tale in the skimmed

Yard of the buttermilk rain on the pail! The sermon

Of blood! The bird loud vein! The saga from mermen

To seraphim

Leaping! The gospel rooks! All tell, this night, of him

Who comes as red as the fox and sly as the heeled wind.

Illumination of music! The lulled black backed

Gull, on the wave with sand in its eyes! And the foal moves

Through the shaken greensward lake, silent, on moonshod hooves,

In the winds' wakes.

Music of elements, that a miracle makes!

Earth, air, water, fire, singing into the white act,

The haygold haired, my love asleep, and the rift blue

Eyed, in the haloed house, in her rareness and hilly

High riding, held and blessed and true, and so stilly

Lying the sky

Might cross its planets, the bell weep, night gather her eyes,

The Thief fall on the dead like the willy-nilly dew,

Only for the turning of the earth in her holy

燃烧！夜晚，鸟在林中翻飞，血脉奔涌！
透过田间的翠花秀叶，血液不停地搏动！
小溪流自牧师黑手腕的灌木林，流自
　　　　　　　夜莺喧闹的童话中
含霜蓟丛的袖管！幽谷的孤魂声嘶力竭地歌唱！
松柏丛生的小山斜披白色的法袍！

喧闹的童话涉掠的庭院里，奶汁
雨点般敲打着奶桶！血的布道！
血脉响亮的飞鸟！英雄传奇从人鱼
　　　　　　　跃向六翼天使！
传播福音的白嘴鸦！今夜的一切都在诉说
他的降临，狐狸般猩红，尾风般隐秘而狡诈。

音乐的启示！宁静的黑脊海鸥
眼含沙砾飞翔于碧波之上！小马驹掠过
绿意颤栗的湖面，寂静的月光马蹄声碎，
　　　　　　　清风令人警觉。
音乐的一切元素创造大自然的奇迹！
泥土、空气、流水和烈火诵唱白色的一幕，

我梦中的心肝宝贝，头发干草般金黄，双眸
透出一丝蔚蓝，室内光影浮动，她独自驰骋
在高高的山岗，纯真而尽享神的祝福，天空
　　　　　　　静静地展卧，
也许划过行星，钟声哭泣，夜晚聚拢她的目光，
那个贼像露水般不容分说地降临死尸，

只为转动她神圣心灵中的世界！

Heart! Slyly, slowly, hearing the wound in her side go
Round the sun, he comes to my love like the designed snow,
                    And truly he
Flows to the strand of flowers like the dew's ruly sea,
And surely he sails like the ship shape clouds. Oh he

Comes designed to my love to steal not her tide raking
Wound, nor her riding high, nor her eyes, nor kindled hair,
But her faith that each vast night and the saga of prayer
                    He comes to take
Her faith that this last night for his unsacred sake
He comes to leave her in the lawless sun awaking

Naked and forsaken to grieve he will not come.
Ever and ever by all your vows believe and fear
My dear this night he comes and night without end my dear
                    Since you were born:
And you shall wake, from country sleep, this dawn and each first dawn,
Your faith as deathless as the outcry of the ruled sun.

他隐秘而狡诈，听到她腰间的伤口绕着太阳
而转动，慢慢地走向我的心肝，犹如谋划的冬雪，
他正走向鲜花
盛开的河岸，像露水流入秩序井然的大海，
他肯定要出航，犹如船形的云朵。哦，他正

谋划着靠近我的宝贝，不去偷取她的海潮去冲刷
伤口，也不去偷取她的驰骋，她的双眸，她点燃的秀发，
而是偷取她的信仰，每一个辽远的夜晚以及
祈祷者的传奇，
就在昨夜他带走她的信仰，为他并不神圣的目的，
在非法的阳光苏醒之际，他又将她遗弃，

让她独自赤裸着身，哀叹他的离去
无论你如何信誓旦旦，不管你是相信还是害怕，
我的心肝宝贝，今夜他正走来，自从你降临人世
夜晚永不停息：
你会从梦中的乡村醒来，在黎明以及每个最初的黎明，
你的信仰永生不灭，仿佛受制的太阳爆发的呐喊。

Over Sir John's Hill

Over Sir John's hill,

The hawk on fire hangs still;

In a hoisted cloud, at drop of dusk, he pulls to his claws

And gallows, up the rays of his eyes the small birds of the bay

And the shrill child's play

Wars

Of the sparrows and such who swansing, dusk, in wrangling hedges.

And blithely they squawk

To fiery tyburn over the wrestle of elms until

The flash the noosed hawk

Crashes, and slowly the fishing holy stalking heron

In the river Towy below bows his tilted headstone.

Flash, and the plumes crack,

And a black cap of jack-

Daws Sir John's just hill dons, and again the gulled birds hare

To the hawk on fire, the halter height, over Towy's fins,

In a whack of wind.

There

Where the elegiac fisherbird stabs and paddles

In the pebbly dab-filled

Shallow and sedge, and 'dilly dilly,' calls the loft hawk,

在约翰爵爷的山岗上^①

在约翰爵爷的山岗上，
燃烧的雄鹰默默地盘旋；
云雾升腾，暮色降临，他伸展威慑的
利爪，锐利的目光触及港湾上飞翔的小鸟，
触及尖叫的孩子戏斗的
麻雀
以及那些在黄昏嘈杂的灌木篱上天鹅般哀鸣的飞禽。
它们咯咯地欢叫
跳上角斗的榆树林上火热的刑场
直到入套的雄鹰猛然
出击，山下托依河^②里昂首阔步
悠然潜行的圣鹭垂首于倾斜的墓碑。

猛然一击，羽毛飞散，
约翰爵爷公正的山岗阁下
戴上一顶寒鸦的黑帽，受骗的鸟群再次快速飞向
燃烧的雄鹰，飞向高悬的刑架，一阵狂风掠过
托依河上闪亮的鱼鳍。
那儿
悲哀的鱼鹰入水觅食
踱步在卵石比目鱼密布的
浅滩和芦苇荡，"宝贝，宝贝"，空中的雄鹰呼唤，

① 1949 年 5 月首次发表于《博特奥斯克》。
② 托依河（River Towy），位于英国拉恩（Laugharne），狄兰·托马斯晚年
居住的小镇。

'Come and be killed,'
I open the leaves of the water at a passage
Of psalms and shadows among the pincered sandcrabs prancing

And read, in a shell,
Death clear as a bouy's bell:
All praise of the hawk on fire in hawk-eyed dusk be sung,
When his viperish fuse hangs looped with flames under the brand
Wing, and blest shall
Young
Green chickens of the bay and bushes cluck, 'dilly dilly,
Come let us die.'
We grieve as the blithe birds, never again, leave shingle and elm,
The heron and I,
I young Aesop fabling to the near night by the dingle
Of eels, saint heron hymning in the shell-hung distant

Crystal harbour vale
Where the sea cobbles sail,
And wharves of water where the walls dance and the white cranes stilt.
It is the heron and I, under judging Sir John's elmed
Hill, tell-tale the knelled
Guilt
Of the led-astray birds whom God, for their breast of whistles,
Have mercy on,
God in his whirlwind silence save, who marks the sparrows hail,
For their souls' song.
Now the heron grieves in the weeded verge. Through windows

"请过来受死"，
我打开水的页面，翻到圣歌
及其阴影的章节，周围的沙蟹伸展利螯欢快地爬动。

阅读，一枚贝壳里，
死亡浮标铃一样清晰：
在鹰眼的黄昏不断地诵唱，赞美燃烧的雄鹰，
在火红的翅翼下垂悬他恶毒的导火线，
赐福
于
港湾和灌木丛中咯咯欢叫的年幼无知的小鸡，
"宝贝，宝贝，请过来一起受死"。
我们感到悲哀，因为欢乐的鸟群从此离别石滩和榆树，
苍鹭和我，
我年轻的伊索①，在鳗鱼的幽谷旁，面对临近的夜晚
讲述寓言，神圣的苍鹭颂唱在贝壳垂挂的远方，

在港湾般透明的幽谷
大海的卵石升起风帆，
在水域码头，岸墙跃动，白鹤亭亭玉立。
苍鹭和我，在法官约翰爵爷的榆树山下，
揭示迷途的
鸟群
犯下的罪孽，上帝因为它们嗯哨的胸脯
宽恕它们，
听到麻雀的呼唤，因那灵魂之歌拯救它们，
上帝刮起的旋风一片宁静。
此刻悲哀的苍鹭立在杂草丛生的岸边。

① 伊索（Aesop），公元前6世纪古希腊著名的寓言家。

Of dusk and water I see the tilting whispering

Heron, mirrored, go,
As the snapt feathers snow,
Fishing in the tear of the Towy. Only a hoot owl
Hollows, a grassblade blown in cupped hands, in the looted elms
And no green cocks or hens
Shout
Now on Sir John's hill. The heron, ankling the scaly
Lowlands of the waves,
Makes all the music; and I who hear the tune of the slow,
Wear-willow river, grave,
Before the lunge of the night, the notes on this time-shaken
Stone for the sake of the souls of the slain birds sailing.

透过黄昏和流水之窗，我看到俯身低语的苍鹭

映着河水，捕食
在托依河的泪水中，
而折断的羽毛雪花般飘舞。只有猫头鹰
哀鸣在劫后的榆树林，一片草叶吹入合拢的手心，
此刻约翰爵爷的山岗
不再有
幼稚的雄鸟或雌鸟在啼鸣。苍鸳，走在
波光粼粼的洼地，
奏出所有的乐音；我聆听岸柳相间的河水
缓缓流动的旋律，
在夜晚袭来之前，在这时光摇撼的石头上掩埋
那些音符，为了蒙难鸟群的灵魂安然出航。

In the White Giant's Thigh

Through throats where many rivers meet, the curlews cry,
Under the conceiving moon, on the high chalk hill,
And there this night I walk in the white giant's thigh
Where barren as boulders women lie longing still

To labour and love though they lay down long ago.

Through throats where many rivers meet, the women pray,
Pleading in the waded bay for the seed to flow
Though the names on their weed grown stones are rained away,

And alone in the night's eternal, curving act
They yearn with tongues of curlews for the unconceived
And immemorial sons of the cudgelling, hacked

Hill. Who once in gooseskin winter loved all ice leaved
In the courters' lanes, or twined in the ox roasting sun
In the wains tonned so high that the wisps of the hay
Clung to the pitching clouds, or gay with anyone
Young as they in the after milking moonlight lay

Under the lighted shapes of faith and their moonshade
Petticoats galed high, or shy with the rough riding boys,

在白色巨人的大腿间[①]

透过众多河流汇集的咽喉，麻鹬鸣叫着，
在高高的白垩色山岗上，受孕的月光下，
今夜我行走在白色巨人的大腿间，
那卵石般贫瘠的女人们静静地躺着，

渴望生育渴望爱情，尽管她们躺下已久。

透过众多河流汇集的咽喉，女人们祈祷，
祈求种子漂进那蹚过的港湾，
尽管雨水已洗去杂草丛生的石块上的大名，

孤单地躺在无尽的夜晚，蜷缩着身子，
她们舔着麻鹬的舌头，渴望的儿子尚未怀上，
他们在远古的山岗，靠刀棍砍伐树林。

她们曾在鹅皮般的冬天，在求爱的小道
恋上所有的冰叶，或在烤肉般的阳光下，
在高高的马车上成双成对，车上满载的干草
触及垂落的云彩，或与哪位年轻人寻欢作乐，
躺在被点燃的信念之下，月光如流淌的乳汁，

月影下她们的衬裙被风高高地吹起，
或因一旁粗野的马夫羞红了脸，

① 1950 年 9 月为一广播剧而创作。

狄兰·托马斯诗选

Dylan Thomas

273

Now clasp me to their grains in the gigantic glade,

Who once, green countries since, were a hedgerow of joys.

Time by, their dust was flesh the swineherd rooted sly,
Flared in the reek of the wiving sty with the rush
Light of his thighs, spreadeagle to the dunghill sky,

Or with their orchard man in the core of the sun's bush
Rough as cows' tongues and thrashed with brambles their buttermilk
Manes, under the quenchless summer barbed gold to the bone,

Or rippling soft in the spinney moon as the silk
And ducked and draked white lake that harps to a hail stone.

Who once were a bloom of wayside brides in the hawed house
And heard the lewd, wooed field flow to the coming frost,
The scurrying, furred small friars squeal, in the dowse
Of day, in the thistle aisles, till the white owl crossed

Their breast, the vaulting does roister, the horned bucks climb
Quick in the wood at love, where a torch of foxes foams,
All birds and beasts of the linked night uproar and chime

And the mole snout blunt under his pilgrimage of domes,

Or, butter fat goosegirls, bounced in a gambo bed,
Their breasts full of honey, under their gander king
Trounced by his wings in the hissing shippen, long dead

此刻她们抱紧我，向着大片林间空地上的谷物，

那也曾是绿色原野上快乐的篱笆墙。

时光荏苒，她们的尘土是猪倌暗地扎根的血肉，
嫁在猪圈闻着臭味，却因他双腿冲刺的光芒
而燃烧，面对污秽的天空鹰翼般张开，

或是相伴果园里的情人，在阳光的杂树丛
狂暴如母牛狂舐，随荆棘的枝条颠摇奶酪般的
灵魂，夏日般不熄的热情如金钩直达肉骨，

或在月光下的小树林如丝般轻轻波动，
野鸭游弋的白色湖面因冰雹般的石子激起琴声阵阵。

她们曾是路边的新娘如花般盛开在山楂装点的新房，
听到淫荡的求爱园溺没在寒霜下，急匆匆的小修士
一身浓毛，在暮色苍苍、紫蓟丛生的走廊里
发出喜悦的尖叫，直到白色的猫头鹰掠过

她们的乳胸，穿顶下喧闹一片，长角的公羊爬上来，
飞快窜入做爱的树林，狐狸的火炬喷涌白沫，
连环的夜晚里，所有的飞禽走兽和睦地喧闹，

而鼹鼠的尖嘴笨拙地拱起对圆穹顶的朝圣，

或者，黄油般肥胖的牧鹅女，跃动在摇床，
双乳涨满蜂蜜，在嘶嘶作响的鹅棚里
承接雄鹅王翅翼不断的拍击，那片黑暗的

And gone that barley dark where their clogs danced in the spring,
And their firefly hairpins flew, and the ricks ran round—

(But nothing bore, no mouthing babe to the veined hives
Hugged, and barren and bare on Mother Goose's ground
They with the simple Jacks were a boulder of wives)—

Now curlew cry me down to kiss the mouths of their dust.

The dust of their kettles and clocks swings to and fro
Where the hay rides now or the bracken kitchens rust
As the arc of the billhooks that flashed the hedges low
And cut the birds' boughs that the minstrel sap ran red.
They from houses where the harvest kneels, hold me hard,
Who heard the tall bell sail down the Sundays of the dead
And the rain wring out its tongues on the faded yard,
Teach me the love that is evergreen after the fall leaved
Grave, after Beloved on the grass gulfed cross is scrubbed
Off by the sun and Daughters no longer grieved
Save by their long desires in the fox cubbed
Streets or hungering in the crumbled wood: to these
Hale dead and deathless do the women of the hill
Love forever meridian through the courters' trees

And the daughters of darkness flame like Fawkes fires still.

麦地早已消逝，春天里她们的木屐曾在那舞动，
她们萤火虫般的发夹飞落，干草垛跟着旋转——

（但什么都未孕育，没有婴儿紧抱血脉的蜂巢
吮吸，鹅妈妈赤裸的土地上荒凉贫瘠，
她们是质朴的杰克那卵石般的妻子）——

此刻麻鹬的哀鸣让我俯身亲吻她们尘土的嘴唇。

她们的水罐和时钟上的尘埃飘来荡去，
此刻干草漂浮，羊齿长满锈迹斑斑的厨房，
犹如钩镰的弧口，它们曾削低了篱笆，
切割鸟群的枝条，让游吟诗人口流红色的树液。
她们从丰收下跪的房室将我紧紧地拥抱，
听到响亮的钟声驶过死者的一个个礼拜天
雨水在颓败的院落里拧干自己的口舌，
她们告诉我爱情常青，即便树叶落满坟地，
阳光擦洗失落于草丛的十字基督，
女儿们不再悲伤，她们仍然会
在狐狸生养的大街滋生起欲望，
或在碎败的树林里饥肠辘辘：
山岗上的女人将穿过求爱者的树林，
永远疯狂地热恋那些健壮不灭的死者，

黑暗中的女儿像福克斯①的火药静静地燃烧。

① 福克斯（Guy Fawkes），1605 年曾策划并执行伦敦臭名昭著的火药阴谋，
  试图炸掉英国国会大厦引发叛乱。随后每年 11 月 5 日，英国人举行"福
  克斯之夜"，即焰火之夜或大篝火之夜，庆祝阴谋被粉碎。

Elegy

Too proud to die; broken and blind he died
The darkest way, and did not turn away,
A cold kind man brave in his narrow pride

On that darkest day. Oh, forever may
He lie lightly, at last, on the last, crossed
Hill, under the grass, in love, and there grow

Young among the long flocks, and never lie lost
Or still all the numberless days of his death, though
Above all he longed for his mother's breast

Which was rest and dust, and in the kind ground
The darkest justice of death, blind and unblessed.
Let him find no rest but be fathered and found,

I prayed in the crouching room, by his blind bed,
In the muted house, one minute before
Noon, and night, and light. The rivers of the dead

Veined his poor hand I held, and I saw
Through his unseeing eyes to the roots of the sea.

挽　歌①

傲然不屑死去；失明而心碎地死去，
他走上最黑暗之路，不再回头，
一位勇敢而善良的人，冷峻而孤傲，

那一天最黑暗。哦，愿他从此躺下，
终于能轻松地躺下，最终穿越山岗，
在青草之下，永沐爱意，在那长长的

人群中勃发青春，决不迷失
或沉寂在那死亡无穷无尽的岁月，
尽管他依然渴望母亲的乳汁，

最终安息并化为尘土，仁慈的大地上
死亡那最黑暗的公正，盲目又不幸。
让他不屑安息，却被生养，重返人世，

在沉默的屋内，蜷缩的内室间，
在他失明的病榻边，我祈祷
在正午、夜晚和黎明前的那一刻，

死亡之河在我握住的可怜的手心流淌，
透过他看不见的眼睛，我看到大海之根。

① 1952 年 12 月 16 日，父亲的去世让诗人留下这首《挽歌》，1953 年 12 月诗人的不幸离去使得这首诗成了永久的残片。1956 年 2 月，该诗首次发表于《邂逅》。

狄兰·托马斯诗选

Dylan Thomas

279

[An old tormented man three-quarters blind,

I am not too pround to cry that He and he
Will never never go out of my mind.
All his bones crying, and poor in all but pain,

Being innocent, he dreaded that he died
Hating his God, but what he was was plain:
An old kind man brave in his burning pride.

The sticks of the house were his; his books he owned.
Even as a baby he had never cried;
Nor did he now, save to his secret wound.

Out of his eyes I saw the last light glide.
Here among the light of the lording sky
An old blind man is with me where I go

Walking in the meadows of his son's eye
On whom a world of ills came down like snow.
He cried as he died, fearing at last the spheres'

Last sound, the world going out without a breath:
Too proud to cry, too frail to check the tears,
And caught between two nights, blindness and death.

O deepest wound of all that he should die
On that darkest day. Oh, he could hide
The tears out of his eyes, too proud to cry.

Until I die he will not leave my side.]

（一个受苦的老人丧失了四分之三视力，

我没那么高傲，不会不屑于哭泣，
上帝和他将永驻我心。
他的骨头在哭泣，除了痛苦，缺乏一切，

他如此天真，害怕死时会
憎恨上帝，他清楚自己是什么样的人：
勇敢、善良、炽热孤傲的垂暮之人。

屋内的手杖是他的；书是他的珍藏。
自打出生起他就从不哭泣；
此刻他也不哭，除了自身的隐痛。

我看见最后一丝光芒滑过他的眼睛。
在这君临天下的光线之中
一位失明的老人随我走上

他儿子目所能及的草地，
不幸的世界像雪片一样降临。
他死去时哭了，最终害怕世上

最后的声音，世界消逝得无声无息：
傲然不屑哭泣，脆弱得无法控制泪水，
深陷于两个夜晚之间，失明与死亡。

哦，至深的痛，莫过于他将会死在
最黑暗的日子。哦，他的眼睛
竟然能藏得住眼泪，傲然不屑哭泣。

直到我死去，他都不会离开我的身旁。）